It will always *BE YOU!*

Dilek Ozlem Ataonder

Hilsea Street
Publishing House

3 Hilsea Publishing House, DOA Agency London.

© Dilek Ozlem Ataonder 2021

ISBN: 978-1-800494-718

All rights reserved

First published 2021

Translated from: Hep Sen Olacaksın

Author: Dilek Ozlem Ataonder

English version Editor: Jane Fricker

Dilek Ozlem Ataonder

Dilek Ozlem Ataonder was born in south Turkey / Hatay in 1983. She graduated from Marmara University, Faculty of Journalism in Istanbul. While still a student, she started her journalism career as a Police and Courts reporter (investigative reporter) for Hurriyet newspaper in 2002.

Ataonder went on to work as an editor and then senior editor for the major media channels Hurriyet, Aksam and Haberturk newspapers and Star TV. In 2015, she established her own company and started working in the media consultancy, corporate communication and PR sector.

Ataonder, who settled in England in 2018, continued her career in London.

Dilek Ozlem Ataonder published her first two books in Turkish, *Benim Bir Hayalim Var mıydı Quasimodo? (Did I Have a Dream, Quasimodo?)* and *Sabaha Karşı Beş Ayazında (In the Morning Frost at Five o'Clock)*, in London in 2020.

Dilek Ozlem Ataonder wrote her third book in Turkish and then translated it herself into English. She published the third book, *It Is Not An Immigrant Story, It Was Always You,* in London in 2021. Ataonder wrote her fourth book, *It Will Always Be You* – the sequel to It Is Not An Immigrant Story, It Was Always You – again translating the text herself into English and published it in London in 2021.

IT WILL ALWAYS BE YOU

Dilek Ozlem ATAONDER

To my dearest...
To my dear mum Feride Ataonder.

Saturday, July 10, 2021

"Life has opened a new page for me today!"
Do you remember the day on which the first book started? And the words I used to start my tale?

I do!

My first story opened with the very same words, "Life has opened a new page for me today! I left Turkey and set foot in England!", and began on July 10, 2018.

Today, on July 10, 2021, three years later, life has opened a new page for me on the very same day. Three years later, I was at Gatwick Airport on the same day with a large suitcase and a handbag. I was counting the seconds backwards,

  Tick, tock,
    Tick, tock,

I was waiting for the moment to pass at midnight, and when the date would click over to July 10, 2021. I had to wait. It was a legal requirement.

I looked at the clock, my soul calm and in silence. It was 00:01, and I was on the threshold of July 10, 2021.

Why did I have to wait for that date, that moment?

What was I doing at Gatwick Airport in the middle of the night?

Why did I have my suitcase with me?

Was I alone?

Was I leaving England, or was I coming back?

Why was I constantly taking ever deeper breaths until my lungs were about to burst?

Why was I starving again? Why was I hungry again?

Was I a 'hunger'?

Why and how did all these chronological coincidences occur?

What had happened to me?

THE BEGGARS OF LOVE

"My dear people, my esteemed employees! Today, I'm here to honour our new chairman of the board, Daniel. He has gone through countless trials and overcome many difficulties since he started working for our enterprises. In our new order, bringing happiness back to the world, he has always succeeded in making his wife, his children, family, friends, and his employees happy, as God expects of us. I'm proud of you, my dear chairman of the board," beamed the speaker, a man probably in his seventies but looking somewhat younger.

When it was Daniel's turn to speak, he smiled awkwardly and began, "As you all know, we have a new president, elected President of our country by your votes last night. He handed over the management of all our companies to me today. Therefore, we will have a big party to celebrate, with you, and other friends at the Presidential Palace tomorrow. I will share with you my feelings then, what these twenty years have meant to me coming up to this moment, to this opportunity being given to me, and what happy days are ahead of us, at the speech I will give at the party. For now, I will rest content with just saying thank you to everyone. Happy tomorrows," and he raised his glass.

Everyone was ecstatic. They took turns congratulating Daniel, without a single glint of envy or jealousy in their eyes. Daniel glanced at his personal chief assistant, Angela, who had come over to him. The voice of the crowd was muffled for a few seconds between them. Daniel took Angela by the shoulders and smiled.

They smiled with their secrets.

After the party was over, Daniel got into his private vehicle. His driver looked at him in the rearview mirror, "Good job, you sickborn. Congratulations," he said.

"Thanks, Peter," Daniel replied.

Peter drove the car home. The vehicle traversed the city's busiest streets, past its restaurants and cafes. As usual, they passed along the edge of Jubilant Park. Daniel was watching out of the window of his car, like always when they drove along the park in the evenings when he made his way home from work. People were sitting on the grass, picnicking, having a drink, chatting with their friends or family. Parents were cheering their children along in the playground; couples were hugging and kissing, in love. They all looked so happy. The purest form of happiness. Of course they were happy because they lived in the city of Felicity, the capital of Ecstatic Land.

Daniel's car stopped at a red light. A young girl was slowly running towards her boyfriend. The girl jumped on the boy's neck; they hugged each other tightly and kissed. It was a reflection of pure love, no lie. Daniel ran his index finger over the window control button as he slowly looked over at them. It was a beautiful sunset outside; he could imagine its colours. He could open the window and see those beautiful colours and listen to those sounds of happiness. But he continued to watch from the grey reflection of his black mirrored window, rather than seeing those false colours and hearing the voices.

***

Then...

She suddenly jumped out of the car!

"What the hell are you doing?" the driver shouted at her.

'I want to buy a coffee."

"You have to tell me if you want to coffee, you sickborn! Get back in the car."

"Just a few minutes, Henry. I'll get a coffee and be right back. Please!"

The red light had turned green, and horns honked from other vehicles. The driver stared angrily at Louise, "I'll park and be right back. You wait for me here, and we will go together."

"Can I walk alone to the elevator?"

"Damn it. Okay. Wait for me there," shouted Henry.

Louise walked quickly to the mall elevator. She was wearing a beautiful, luxurious, olive green silk dress. When she got to the elevator, her eyes quickly searched for Henry, and when she saw that he had just entered the car park, she got into the elevator with the mothers and their babies. The inside of the elevator smelled of baby, utterly. Louise leaned back against the elevator window, touched her pregnant belly, closed her eyes, and took a deep breath. She opened her eyes, took another deep breath, looking at the ground to hide what was inside, more slowly, more deeply. Then she met the eyes of the baby next to her. The baby's mother looked at her as Louise smiled at the infant. With the smile plastered on her face, Louise turned her head towards the elevator window to hide the disgust in her eyes. The elevator stopped at ground level. One of the mothers, getting out of the elevator with her stroller, looked at Louise suspiciously while the other mothers bundled in. Louise was back down on the ground floor, still breathing in that baby scent, standing in the same place. Then she got out of the elevator and waited at the door for Henry, with repulsion in her eyes.

When Henry came towards her, she started to smile again as if nothing had happened. It wasn't easy for her to do this in her disgust, but she had to play her role well, as always, for a very, very long time. When they got their coffee and returned to the car, Henry said to her, "You will have to pray for what you've done."

Louise did not answer him. When they got home, she went straight to her dark, quiet, lonely room. She took off her dress, underwear, and the prosthetic pregnant belly.

***

He had stripped naked. He looked at his body, which had turned into a shadow in the mirror in the darkness. Then he started to walk. There was such silence around him that he could even hear the sound of his body rippling through the air. He stopped by the bookshelf, touched a concealed button, a hidden door opened slowly behind it. His wife and true love were having passionate sex.

Daniel looked at the man, his body and face were as ugly as his soul, but his wife was blindly in love with him. Too insane and blinded to care that the man in front of her was a 'hunter'. They were kissing as if they were about to die. The woman groaned with greater pleasure as the man pressed his body against her. Daniel wondered how they could be so happy with their hideous souls. He was disgusted with the world he lived in, observing how this ugly soul of a man could be so lucky and how he enjoyed such a happy, wealthy life without making a single effort.

He closed the door and returned to the silence and darkness inside his room. He looked at his shadow body again in the reflection of the mirror.

***

She was gorgeous, had a perfect body. Although she was thirty-eight, she looked ten years younger. But she was in the shadows. She quickly turned her head so that she couldn't see any more of that shadow body and went, naked, to the swimming pool, which was one floor below the bedroom. She immersed herself in the water until her body touched the bottom of the pool. She stood there for a while, watching the deep roar of the water, the reflections in front of her. Her heart started beating fast, then slowed down. She stood under the water to the last beat of her heart, and just as it was about to come to a stop, she quickly moved upwards to the surface. As she leant on the side of the pool, trying to catch her breath, her husband came with his pregnant lover, who was never parted from him. They looked at Louise as she stood in the pool, laughing in disdain.

Louise slowly paddled up the steps, and emerged from the pool. Drops streamed from her waist-length black hair down her shoulders, down her erect breasts, down her flawless body, flowing softly from her silky skin.

Calvin approached Louise, came behind her, looked at the drops of water on her shoulder, her bare body, and said, "Pray."
Louise knelt, raised her right hand, opened it like a beggar, "Thank you for giving me this life, success, family, friends that will make my home. Thank you for turning me into 'a complete happy person' by presenting me with this baby. God bless you. God

bless and perpetuate the 'Happy Friday' religion. With every breath I take, I express my gratitude to God, the religion of Happy Friday, my husband Calvin, his soulmate Ashley, their children, family, and friends. Until my last breath."

***

Mary approached Daniel, grabbed him by the chin, and lifted his head toward her. Daniel continued his prayer of thanks, looking into the eyes of Mary and George.

"I am weak. I'm miserable. I am a 'sick born'. I am a 'hunger'."
"Life is too good to come out as a 'hunger', huh? Good boy!
"I have a special surprise for you, Mary. I'm giving it at the party tomorrow, right after my speech. To express my gratitude to you, George, your family and your friends."
"Hopefully, it's a surprise worth waiting for."
"Yes it will be worth it, Mary. All the world will be talking about this surprise for years. Trust me."
"We'll see. Now go back to your room."
"Good night Mary, good night George," he said, smiling.

He went to his room, naked and wet, to his bed and hugged his soft duvet in its silk cover to him. He felt his muscular, strong, perfect body, felt his long legs, avoided feeling that, closed his eyes, and tried to sleep.

After a sleepless night, she went to work. It was hours before the big party, the moment they had been waiting for, for twenty years. Inside was the chaos of all the good and bad feelings that could ever be. She wanted to believe that the anxiety inside her was because that big day was coming. She wanted to be wrong, but she couldn't be wrong! She was one of the 'sick born', as the others called them. Her feelings were all getting worse. She wanted these feelings to be wrong.

Suddenly a video message came through on her phone.

She was in the middle of a meeting, she couldn't open the message, but when she saw who it was from, her face changed colour, her eyes filled with tears knowing that person wouldn't be calling her at this hour unless imperative. She swallowed, stopped the tears from spilling, took a deep breath to calm herself, smiled, and lifted her head. She paused the meeting and quietly went to her room. Her huge glass room faced the open plan office, where she could see the dozens of people she directed. She quickly closed the door and watched the incoming message.

Louise played the video again to understand what had happened to Dustin, who had sent the video. Dustin was screaming, "They found me!"

The scream rang around the room, and then, "They've found you", echoed a voice behind Louise. The sound was coming from the door of Louise's room, which someone had knocked and opened suddenly without permission while she was watching the video.

Louise paused the video, frowned worriedly, raised her eyes in anger.

"They found you too, Louise," the voice squealed, in front of the entire office, clearly ecstatic to find such an important hunger standing there in the room.

Louise turned sharply in the direction of the voice and walked quickly towards it. She knew she had to act very fast so that twenty years of hard work would not be destroyed. She looked at her employees, who were silent, in shock, and at the owner of the voice. She put her hand under her dress, pulled a gun from her fake pregnant belly, took the owner of the voice hostage.

The soldiers had arrived already.

Pulling the woman along who had found her with a gun to her forehead, Louise opened the door of the fire escape next to her room and shouted at the top of her voice, "Yes, you found me. I'm a hunger. I'm a fucking hunger, and here is your reward." She pushed the woman away from her with an unexpected movement and fired a single shot into her forehead. Then she threw herself from the 33rd floor through the gap at the edge of the fire escape amid the soldiers' shots and the screams of the employees.

***

Angela closed the door to drown out the shouts and noise of the crowd. Daniel stood up, they hugged each other, and they looked into each other's eyes. Daniel stroked Angela's hair and touched her cheeks. They placed their hands over their hearts. They listened to their hearts, they felt.

And they hugged.

They hugged tightly as if they were seeing each other for the last time, hugging each other for the last time.

Like when they had seen each other in the 'beggar tunnels' and hugged for the very first time.

She stood in front of the beggar tunnels, looked at her dark shadow. Her white dress was smeared with blood from the gunshot wound to her abdomen. She had taken off her high heels so that she could run faster with her injured ankle. She was out of breath as she ran as fast as she could so that the 'soldiers of happiness' and their agents wouldn't catch her.

"Here!" someone shouted, pointing at her. As the soldiers rushed towards her and fired, the people were watching them with curiosity. She was not supposed to be caught, and without a second thought, she went into the tunnel.

As she walked in the darkness, she could hear people shouting, "She's gone, surrendered."

She walked in pitch black for a while. She started to gag because of that disgusting smell. She could barely breathe. Her bare feet were bumping against something on the wet and sticky floor. She couldn't see in the darkness, but she knew they were dead bodies. A bottomless silence fell in her ears. When the entrance door disappeared, she turned on her cell phone torch and saw them.

She saw *the beggars of love*.

She couldn't move from the spot for several minutes. Then overcome with nausea she knelt to the ground and began to vomit. As she emptied her stomach and tried to stand up, she saw the vomit sticking to her palm on the ground. She began to vomit again with a sudden growling until bitter bile juice spilled from her throat again. When she got up, she was dizzy from the unbearable stench inside and the lack of oxygen. She couldn't bear it and started to cry. Her sobs echoed around that endless tunnel.

She tried to calm herself, looked around again, and knelt beside a beggar of love who was slumped against the tunnel wall. She shone the light from her phone on the man's face, into his eyes, but he didn't even blink. Flies covered the man's eyes, nose, ears and face. When she got closer to him she realized that he was breathing. Louise was sure that the man was still alive. She began to glide the light over the man's body, his skin dry and wrinkled, his bones and even the thinnest capillaries visible. His body, like his face, was covered with dried vomit and flies crawling over him. She searched for a single movement, an expression in the man's eyes, face, body, but all she could see was emptiness, an empty dead body breathing.

Louise's eyes were torn wide open as she turned the light toward the woman next to the man. Half of whose cheek had already vanished, the other parts of her cheek were covered with maggots. The woman was being eaten alive by those maggots. Louise leaned in close with her nose, sniffing her body and breath. She smelled what it meant to be a hunger and then a beggar of love. She felt sick again with that smell, and bitter bile juice came back up from her empty stomach. She straightened herself up, brought the light close to the woman's cheek, and watched how the maggots were eating her alive. They had transparent dark cream coloured bodies and small black eyes. They were tiny but disgusting and innumerable. Some had invaded part of the woman's cheek, revealing rotten flesh from the red to the purple to the black. Some of them made small holes in the areas where they had just started their feast and went in and out of those gaps. Others had amassed into a small lump nestled in the woman's lip and were moving like cream-coloured dots in the bloody inflamed sediment that turned brown in the entrance cavity of that lump. They were eating her alive cell by cell.

Louise stood trembling, unable to breathe from the foul smell and lack of oxygen. While trying to stand up, dizzy, about to faint, she raised her hand in the air, illuminating the tunnel with the torch from her phone, staring at the thousands of 'beggars of love' lying on the ground, a mass of skeletons and decomposed bodies, or lying on their backs of dried skin and bones against the walls of the tunnel and being eaten alive.

"Was that possible? Was it possible for those maggots to eat people alive without dying?" thought Daniel as he looked at them. He knew that about an hour after one died, flies began to hover over dead bodies. After the flies ate the cells in the skin of the dead bodies and fed their stomachs, they laid their eggs in those bodies. Just a day later, those eggs would hatch into a colony of thousands of larvae and begin to devour the corpse. As they feast on that body, they create great heat and constantly change places to cool themselves, thus making that dead body appear to move.

But would that be possible before death?

They must have suffered, but when Daniel looked again into the eyes of the 'the beggars of love', all he could see was surrender. At that moment, he realized that he could not forget what he saw and would live with this memory for the rest of his life. He leaned his back on the tunnel, and started to cry.

After a while, he saw a shadow move, but he thought the pitch-black was playing a trick on his eyes. Still, he couldn't help looking towards that spot. As he wiped his tears, that shadow moved again. He stood up, stepped over the dead bodies, and approached the shadow. As he got closer, he realized that the shadow was a woman. The woman standing in front of him in tears, was not yet covered by flies. Realizing that she had arrived there a short time ago he moved closer. He began to cry again, trembling with sadness. The person standing before Daniel was a young girl, no more than sixteen years old. She resembled an angel. She was too young to become a 'beggar of love' and fall into the beggar tunnels.

This shouldn't have happened.

Daniel held out his hand towards her but then pulled back. He looked into her pain-filled eyes and again extended his hand, but he couldn't reach out to her. He was also hunted, he was a hunger, and with that huge emptiness in his heart, he didn't know how to reach his hand out to someone again; he didn't know how to hug someone again.

But he didn't want to give up.

When he realized that he couldn't do it alone, he looked at the girl again, her eyes pleading for help. The girl's tears and sobs abated. She straightened up, stretching her arms towards Daniel, afraid but still in the purest form of the world.

And they hugged each other.

They hugged each other in a truly loving way.

***

After dark, Louise sneaked to the edge of Ecstasy Park. She plunged into the blue lilac flowers that surrounded the park; a small area moved, a secret door opened up on the ground. Louise went in, and the fragrant flower of happiness closed behind her. The lights came on as Louise moved her hands quickly left and right. After walking through the narrow, long corridors for about twenty minutes, she came to a door. She swiped the device in a secret slot on the wall and opened the door.

As soon as she entered, she fell to her knees and began to cry. But she didn't have much time to cry, and quickly recovering herself she stood up. She needed to clean the gunshot wound in her stomach, the smell and the dirt on her. Knowing what to do, first of all, she went to the bathroom, for she remembered what she had to do first, from when she was eighteen, when she could get out of the beggar tunnels. She opened the drawer under the sink, grabbed the razor, and shaved her head to get rid of the worms that had stuck to her hair and scalp, trying not to look at her vomit-stained face. Then she opened the other drawer, took out a special soap from a box, immersed herself in boiling water and washed her body with that soap as if scraping her skin away.

When she came out of the bathroom, her body still covered in blood, she sat on the bed and stitched up the bullet wound that had pierced the left side of her abdomen. She cleaned her body again in the bathroom, not touching the stitches, and dressed. She was exhausted, had lost a lot of blood, but she knew she might faint if she lay down. She took a syringe from the medicine cabinet, drew the drug into it, and slapped her arm. She took six different pills. She had to stand up.

She sat in front of the monitors and looked at what the people in her house were doing from the bunker hidden five floors below. Her husband and his true love were lying next to each other and hugging on the big sofa in the reading room. She zoomed in on them, staring at the serenity on their faces for a few seconds. Louise was expressionless as she always was when she looked at them. It was impossible to understand what she was thinking at that moment. Envy, jealousy, longing, hatred, hate, enmity, revenge… What had filled that massive void in her heart? What emotion had nurtured and grown in that wounded space?

Her brows suddenly furrowed as she continued to stare at them. She felt something strange. She felt a weird pain in the sole of her foot. She placed her left foot on her right knee and looked at the sole of her foot.

She gulped.

She had not realized until that moment that her bare foot had been injured while walking in the tunnel, and the maggots had penetrated deep into that wound.

Louise stared at the way their little bodies moved through the deep wound in her foot.

Daniel continued to stare at those maggots in their tuxedos and posh, stylish evening dresses for a while. The time had come when he no longer needed to hide his gaze. The private party to celebrate the new President and Daniel's chairmanship had begun. Daniel had stepped onto the giant stage in the middle of the Presidential Palace. When the music stopped, he tapped a spoon on his champagne glass. All those maggots turned towards him to listen to his speech as he looked at them with in a look of disgust.

Daniel began his speech, "Dear President, my deputies, administrators, their beloved families, all my esteemed guests… Welcome, all of you, to this historic night. Everyone knows that we are gathered here today for two important things that will change the fate of our country and, therefore, the world. Twenty years ago, two years after my father and you laid the foundations for today's 'happy' world, I promised myself that I would imitate you and change the world, like you, by giving this speech one day."

Whispers broke out among the guests. They were beginning to hear words very different from the speech they had been waiting for. The new president frowned anxiously at Daniel's last sentence.

"In the very first years, I had no idea how to keep that promise I made to myself. Even if I was one of you, among you, it was a utopian dream. But I did it, and I'm here today. I want to show you what this success, this speech and this party really mean to me," he said, raising his left hand, and suddenly the curtains hiding seven giant screens surrounding the reception hall opened.

While everyone was trying to understand what was happening, the lights were dimmed, the lights of those giant screens came on. The door to the largest of the beggar tunnels inside Ecstasy Park appeared on the screen. This time, as the guests began to shout, trying to understand what was happening, men in black clothes and black helmets entered the reception hall holding their big black machine guns. The guests did not know, but those black-clad soldiers had already surrounded the entire palace, streets, city, country, seven continents of the world.

A tsunami of screams surrounded the Presidential Palace as the guests rushed to flee. One of the soldiers fired a bullet from his machine gun into the air and shouted, "Everyone stand still, be quiet and listen to Daniel." Within seconds, everyone fell silent, trembling with fear, mingling with silent tears.

"As you know, two hunger were caught today. They escaped, although they were both wounded by soldiers of happiness. Both of them went to the beggar tunnels and surrendered. Of course we were all relieved because, as you know, not a single person has returned from those tunnels in twenty years.

"As you all know!
"But…" he said, raising his hand again.

The video that Louise shot in the beggar's tunnel on

the same day started playing on the screen. The audience started screaming and retching.

"But some people managed to get back from there. Twenty years ago, I couldn't stand my pain, the games you started on me, your new world orders, and I surrendered, went to that first tunnel you opened in Jubilant Park. After what I saw there that day, I accepted that I would never become a normal person again, as I leant back against the wall of the tunnel and waited for the moment when the flies would cover me.

"But then I saw a young girl in there. She was like an angel. Despite the pain in her eyes in the darkness of that tunnel, she looked at me with eyes that showed she wanted to live. Even though we were both hunted and hunger, we could open our arms and hug each other. With that hug that day, a new world order began despite all your efforts, games, agents, soldiers, weapons, and power.

"Against all powers, you lost!

"You have had your happy world for twenty years and your fucking idiotic 'Happy Friday Religion'. It took me twenty years to build a secret new world from your murderous world where you force more and more people into tunnels and slaughter babies.

"Now I want to show you the real happiness that your world has secretly created. Let's get the party started," he said with a smile.

The screenshots changed; a women appeared on each of the seven screens. Louise, Angela, Carla, Keilee, Marcella, Alessia, Dustin. Seven warriors from seven different continents. With armies of thousands of soldiers behind them, they were waiting at the head of their regions in the seven different continents of the world. Shortly after they appeared on the screens, a massive explosion occurred. The sky lit up with the explosion, turned red, the vast chandeliers and windows of the palace shook, the guests fell to the ground screaming.

One of the guests stood up and started punching one of the soldiers, screaming, "You are all sick born, miserable hungers." The soldier put his gun to the man's forehead and killed him with a single shot. The guests fell into a deep silence, one of the soldiers shouted, "Everyone kneel!" They all did as they were told; they knelt down and raised their right hands, palms open.

One after another, explosions appeared on the screens and around the palace. The sky was as bright as day, turning into a red-orange mottled flame. The flames of freedom, growing and multiplying with each explosion, lighting up Louise, Angela, Carla, Keilee, Marcella, Alessia, Dustin's shaven heads, their faces, enveloping their bodies. Each arm of flame had started to destroy bit by bit the world that they had had to endure for twenty years of hunger, humiliation, insults, pleading, hiding: those maggots that clung to their existence and devoured them alive. Every explosion, spark, tongue of flame was trying to clean the wounds in their eyes, minds, skin, and souls, filling the great void that was constantly bleeding and aching in their hearts.

The explosions and deafening rattles of machine guns roared out from the seven screens and outside the Presidential Palace. The guests were trembling more and more, crying, screaming and begging. Screams, pleading, cries were heard from all sides.

Neither Daniel, Louise, Angela, Carla, Keilee, Marcella, Alessia, Dustin, nor the soldiers heard or saw their cries or pleas. For twenty years, they had been hunted, called *hunger, 'beggars of love', 'sick born'*, and had to hide.

Was it possible for them to hear those voices? Was it possible that they still had a heart after all that?

Despite all they'd been through, had they managed to carry a heart again in those huge voids in their breasts?

What would they do?

What would happen to Daniel, his seven warriors on seven continents, the soldiers, those in the Presidential Palace, and the rest of the people outside, to all the world?

Why did all this happen? How did the world change in this way twenty years ago? What has happened in those twenty years? How did all these *hunted* and *hunger* find each other? How did they hide? How and why had they waited twenty years?

What would happen now?

Once upon a time, the world was the same as it had always been: one part of the world had hunger, drought, misery, natural disasters, wars. Newborn babies were dying in their mothers' arms. While playing on the street, children were injured by bombs, losing limbs. Young people could not even learn to dream about the future in this monstrous world. Although hell was explained in the scriptures as a place for bad people after they die, good people lived with unimaginable pain in this hellish reality.

In other parts, away from this hell, people lived in developed societies in developed countries. They were happy! Looking from the outside! But in fact, to comply with the rules of the developed society in those developed societies, more concessions were demanded of them and they were losing themselves more and more. Ordinary people were getting ruder and ruder, more competitive, biased, monstrous, day by day, for the sake of work, food, health, education, success, a better career, more power and money. They were closing their eyes and ignoring the problems in the hells of the world, in their own heavens.

While all of this was going on, someone was getting richer, stronger, and had strong, richer, happier days in their luxurious lives.

Humanity had already rotted, maybe it always was, and with this rottenness, people were killing and leaving each other, the animals and nature to rot, more and more.

And they were calling it *'life'*.

And those who could not keep up with so-called 'life' and who became sad, unhappy, vocal, objecting, protesting or rebelling, were called emotional, touchy, incompatible, asocial, depressed, mentally ill. Emotional, touchy, maladaptive, asocial, depressed, mentally ill people who could not keep up with this ordinary life order were seeking out psychologists more and more each day, trying to get down to their childhood and analyse the traumas there. Those who could not solve these traumas with psychologists needed psychiatric support and became addicted to antidepressant pills on prescription. They were able to see the words kindliness, compassion, understanding, tolerance, helpfulness, friendship and love with their new meanings, whose meanings changed in the dictionary many years ago with those small pills. They were able to equate those feelings with 'weakness' to ordinary life problems and smile again.

They smiled,
            with the frivolous look in their eyes.

Many of those who could not do this consoled themselves with alcohol, drugs, noisy crowded parties, shallow friendships, social status marriages, and children they brought into the world, even if they did not want them. They were comforting themselves with more unhappy relationships, more alcohol, more cocaine, more MDMA, more drugs. They were not able to show the feelings of love, understanding, and sensitivity, which were seen as a weakness, the warm hugs that could be given with those feelings, the sincere smiles, without taking those tiny pills and drugs. They continued to live in their 'modern world', falling into more unhappiness and loneliness with each passing day.

That's how the world and life were, the usual. Without any problem. People watched the news on television, on social media, with or without comment, leaving or not an emoji, talking or not about what happened for a few minutes during the day. Sometimes they participated in protests organized with a handful of people or completely ignored it and continued their daily lives, the 'ordinary world order'.

While the world continued in this ordinary life order as it has been for thousands of years, people were proud of the robotic soldier dogs coming slowly into their lives, watching the first tourists who went to Mars and ever advancing technology and science. But at the same time, they did not believe that in such advanced technology-science, a vaccine could be found in one year for a microscopic virus that caused the death of hundreds of thousands of people. They were holding protests saying "They will chip us", "They will sterilize us", "They will seize our souls and thoughts", "They will rule us", "They will kill us". And the anti-vaxxers called themselves 'smart'.

But they were stupid.

As ordinary people, they were too blind and deaf not to see and understand that our souls and thoughts were seized centuries ago by someone, that we were always managed, that we were unfertilized and robotized many, many years before these vaccines.

They were stupid.
Because they didn't realize that these people who took over and ruled us were actually our Gods.

They were stupid.
Because they didn't realize that our Gods were smart enough not to need to implant chips in our bodies to rule us.

Because our Gods had more amusing, more uncomplicated and more immortal ways to conquer us than chips.

The Gods had phones, televisions, radios, social media, newspapers, networks. So, were these the Gods' ways of capturing humans? Yes, all these communication networks were the soldiers of the Gods; but the Gods were very clever, and they knew that these soldiers would perish, die when the energy was cut off. The Gods were immortal and had an immortal method like themselves. The Gods were invisible and had an invisible way like themselves. The Gods knew inside that in all the crowd, noise, invisible darkness, the biggest, most powerful thing, the only thing that could live forever, that was immortal, were the whispers.

The Gods were whispering to the people.

The Gods had always ruled, they were ruling now, and would continue to wield their power over the people with their whispers.

Everything was going on, as usual, in this way.

Until one day, a man falls madly in love with a woman.

One day a man fell in love with a woman madly and sacrificed everything for her. This young man was only twenty-four, the woman twenty-seven. This young man was the son and only child of one of the richest men in the world. This young man's father had weapons factories, pharmaceutical plants, science-technology bases, ports, ships, colonies, tribes, societies, and communities on seven continents. This young man's father was one of the Gods who ruled the world, and this young man was also a Young God. This Young God's father gave his son, his only heir, the most magnificent education. By the age of twenty-four, this Young God could speak twelve different languages, fluently, like his mother tongue; played dozens of different sports professionally; travelled the world; encountered scores of different cultures; learned history-geography-art better than anyone; took science-technology into his palms. He entered the Gods' Floor under his father's wing to finish his education and become a God deserving of the world his father had to offer.

But this Young God never liked the Gods' Floor, because he was not like the others.

All those fake smiles, hugs, loves, kisses, sex, marriages, deals, collaborations, handshakes, money earned, money spent, all that luxury life seemed to him not wealth but absence.

The wars they started as entertainment, the schemes

they set up, the drug parties, swing games, men's clubs, sex parties, child rape parties, torture parties seemed like powerlessness.

And he knew that no matter what these Gods did, they could not satisfy their souls, and they would not nourish themselves. Because money, power, ego – these three insatiable demons – had taken over their souls.

As this young man saw what the ruling Gods were doing, he hated being a God's heir. Disgusted with everything, he suffered more and more unbearably with each passing day and wanted to escape. And one day, he secretly dressed himself up as an ordinary person, went to an ordinary part of the city, to an ordinary bar; began to drink his ordinary beer among ordinary people.

As the days passed, he became friends with the bartender at the bar he went to. The bartender was a kind-hearted, thirty-something young man who didn't care about power or money and didn't know who the Young God was in reality.

One evening, when the Young God was sitting at that bar with the ordinary people, a woman walked in. With her smooth white skin, blond hair, blue eyes, long, curvy slender body, and pure smile, it was as if an angel has descended to earth. The Young God fell in love the very first moment he saw her. When the young woman stood next to him and hugged the bartender tightly, Young God was upset at first, thinking that she was the bartender's girlfriend. But when the bartender introduced them and said she was his best friend, and the young woman looked into his eyes and smiled warmly, he felt as if he had been born again.

And he continued to feel that way because they fell in love with each other at first sight and were very happy. They loved each other very much, and after only a few months, the Young God could not breathe without her, Nancy. He escaped from the Gods' Floor as he could not stay away from her, not for even a second. When he asked her to marry him as an ordinary person, Nancy happily said, "Yes". They had the happiest day of their lives. They were a couple who had the purest love in the world.

Thereupon, Young God went to his father and told him about Nancy and his decision to marry. Because Nancy was not from the Gods, the Young God's father was distraught and said that if he married Nancy, he would disown him. The Young God asked his mother for help, but his mother, who knew what the anger of the Gods meant and was very afraid of their fury, said that she could not help her son.

Young God had to make a decision, and without a second thought, he chose Nancy. Shortly before they got married, he told Nancy the truth about his life, saying that his father would do anything to turn him away from his decision. Nancy was offended that the Young God had hidden his truth, but then she showed understanding and, holding the hand of the man she loved, they started an ordinary life among ordinary people.

Despite all his talents, Young God was unable to find a job due to interference from his father, Kennedy. When he started working as a bartender for Felix, his best friend, who had introduced him to Nancy, he had to give up the job when his father said he would close that bar. With Young God out of work, Nancy decided to capitalize on the media attention she was gathering for the pair of them. Proving that the love in fairy tales is real, the young couple started giving interviews on television and participating in reality programmes about their lives.

Rejecting all the power and money of the Gods' Floor, their happiness in their one-bedroom flat had begun to spread hope and love to everyone, like a fairy tale come true. Everything was beautiful and pure until Nancy's fifth month of pregnancy when she found out that the baby was a boy. Everything was perfect until Nancy, who had become a 'Sacrifice Goddess' among ordinary people via the media because the Gods did not accept her, started to show her true face. She felt the power that bringing a male heir to that great kingdom would give her.

After her discovery, Nancy began to complain every day of her husband's weakness, of the poverty they were in. The benevolent woman, always smiling at the Young God with pure love, was gone, replaced by a monster who only longed for power and money and revealed that she would do anything for it.

Nancy said to the Young God, "You are the sole heir to the kingdom. No matter how angry your father is with you, he cannot give that kingdom to anyone but you. And I carry that kingdom, that boy who will perpetuate your lineage. They have no choice but to accept me, our marriage and our child. You have to fight your father to take us all to the Gods' Floor." But the Young God protested, telling Nancy he didn't want to go back to the Gods' Floor.

But one day came, and he could not continue his protests any longer. Because Nancy told him, "Maybe you don't want to fight because you got your dad right, huh? For not deeming me worthy of the Gods. If you don't see me worthy there, if your family doesn't accept me, you don't see my baby worthy there either. There is no place in my life for a man who doesn't see us as worthy of the Gods' Floor or who doesn't fight to get my baby and me in there. You don't deserve to be my baby's father and to see him."

Then, she used her power in the media to the full and sobbed on screen in her role as the 'Victim Goddess'. She made the people watching her cry with her, turning the Young God, his father and his family into monsters. Young God's father, Kennedy, had the power to silence Nancy in a single second and erase her from people's memories, but he didn't. Instead, he chose to wait a month. After a month, Kennedy accepted his son and his family.

When Nancy entered the Gods' Floor with her unborn baby and began to live in Kennedy's palace, the beast inside her was fully revealed. Nancy had begun to 'want'. More clothes, more luxurious cars, houses, yachts, jets, and more massive bank accounts…

As Nancy wanted these, the Young God realized that he would never be able to satisfy her. He accepted that Nancy was a victim of power, money, and ego. Still, he chose to remain silent for his unborn son. One day, Kennedy called his son and had a secret meeting with him. When he showed the photographs in his hand to the Young God, Kennedy realized that his son already knew this.

"It's enough!" he said, placing that godly gaze on his son.
"I will solve everything quietly. Just give it some time, for my baby."
"Alright. I will expect you to do whatever you see fit as my son."

After this secret conversation, the Young God went to Nancy, showed her the photos of her kissing Felix.

"We're going to take a long vacation on a private island, and we'll be alone until the baby is born. After the birth, I will take my son, and you will take whatever you want financially… We will get divorced in front of the media as two civilized people who understand that they are not suitable for each other."

"No. You can't tell anyone that I cheated on you. If you reveal that, I will use my power in the media and tell everyone that you and your father are playing a game to kick me out of the Gods' Floor. I won't give my son to you; he is my lifetime guarantee. You can't kick me out of the Gods' Floor."

The Young God approached Nancy, looked into her eyes, "I loved you. From the very first time I saw you, more than anything in the world, even more than the breath I take. But you… It was all a lie; it was an ugly game you played with Felix. But the one thing I can't figure out is how you found out who I am when I met you as an ordinary person."

Nancy laughed, "Your smell!"
"My smell?"
"You can change your clothes and look ordinary, but even if you try to hide amid other scents, the smell of those luxurious perfumes you have on you remains. There was bound to be someone who could smell that scent and question who you really were. It was Felix!"

A deep and sad silence enveloped the Young God. He looked at Nancy with disgust and walked away without saying anything.

The following day, the Young God went to his work, in a meeting with his father as if nothing had happened. At that moment, Kennedy's chief assistant knocked on the door, opened it slowly, fearfully, and said in a shaky voice, "Mr Kennedy, there's breaking news on the TV, and I think you would like to see it."

Kennedy took out the remote in his drawer and pressed the button; a colossal screen slowly opened in the giant room. Saying "You can leave," he sent his assistant out, and he and his son watched the news together. Nancy and Felix has crashed in a car, hurtled off a bridge at full speed as the paparazzi chased them; the car had exploded and they had burned to death. The Young God watched the news silently for a while, then turned to his father and said, "You killed my unborn baby!" his voice hoarse with pain.

"The baby born from such a woman did not deserve to live as your child."

"You knew how much I loved her. You killed my unborn baby."

"I couldn't let any harm come to my kingdom because of your stupid love and that insatiable woman."

And after this accident, the whole world started to change slowly because the Gods had begun to whisper. Screens, papers, voices, mouths were talking about this accident. In the early days, the Gods whispered to the people that Nancy was depressed because of the Young God and his family's exclusion, and she consoled herself in the arms of her lover. Everyone blamed Young God and his family. Whispers turned into shouts, spread to the streets, and organized protests for social justice and against class discrimination.

A month later, the Gods whispered again, and a wind blowing in the opposite direction filled people's mouths. The unlimited wealth Nancy had acquired in the short time after she got married and entered the Gods' Floor spilt out. People talked about how the Young God had a great love for Nancy, how Nancy was changed by her greed for power and money, she actually married the Young God for this reason: that Nancy was actually a *'hunter'*.

Thus, two new words, *'hunters'* and *'hunted'*, were added to the dictionary.

Hunter(s): Who deceive rich people with various tricks, associate with them, marry them if they can persuade them, and thus exploit them materially and morally.

The term 'hunted' has been used for people trapped and exploited by hunters, who suffer for love, and whose hearts are filled with a huge void (emptiness).

Thus, Nancy went into official history as the first known 'hunter' and the Young God as the first 'hunted'. The victim was no longer Nancy but Young God and Kennedy.

Whispers turned into screams, and this time, they jumped into the streets for the Young God. Strangely, people were only talking about them, as if there were no other problems in the world. As a man, he had been deceived by the love of his life, learned the truth with that accident, and as a father who lost his unborn child, the Gods whispered, the Young God had taken his own life. The Gods were working very well, and the whispers were spreading very quickly and powerfully.

A few days after these whispers, a man appeared in the huge park in the centre of the city. "I am a hunted, just like the Young God. I can feel his pain. I am in excruciating pain just like him, and I know it is impossible to live with this pain. Stop hunting people and playing with their emotions," he said and, in the most crowded part of the park, he killed himself with the gun he held to his forehead.

After that day, women and men started killing themselves in the parks and on the streets, screaming, "I am a hunted". The number of these suicides began to increase day by day.

Whispers were blowing people from two different directions. Both cold and hot winds blew in the face of this new mode of psychological behaviour as it took hold. One group of people were thinking: every person has experienced heartbreak at least once in their life. They found it ridiculous to say one can't bear it and to kill oneself. They made fun of the 'hunted', and humiliated them. But another group said they deeply felt their pain, and that human emotions should not be played with.

The whispers of the two groups echoed through the streets into growing screams. People shouted, "Don't disturb society with the unhappiness inside you", "You can't show the pain of your love by killing yourself in front of children in the parks", "If you can't find someone among millions of people who will fall in love with you, it's your own fault!" or "Don't play with our feelings", "Love is not a hunter's game", "Love should not be just a fairy tale".

While these protests were taking place, Kennedy had

Young God, who had locked himself in his room, brought into the hall by force, and made him watch the demonstrations on the streets, on the giant screen.

"I knew it, you would change the world one day," he said to his son, laughing.

At first, the Young God didn't understand what his father meant.

He looked at the screen, then his mother, who was sitting beside his father in silence. After that, he watched his father, who was chuckling as he watched the people killing themselves, cut the thick bloody steak in front of him into big bites with his special knife and pleasurably chew them.

Then he looked at the screen again, at a woman who had just killed herself, and said, "I must do the same."

When the mother of the Young God heard these words, tears began to fall from her eyes in silent fear. Kennedy, who saw the woman crying, became angry.

"That's enough. Are you too stupid to see how we're changing the world? For thousands of years, none of us had found a fun game that would destroy people to such an extent and play with their psychology with such ease. But you did it, my son. Your stupid love and the pain of your love! Come on, let's raise a toast to your success."

But as Young God watched his father, he repeated the same words, "I have to do the same like them."

His mother started to sob again.

"You are both idiots. You both shut up. I order it!"

"I hate you!" cried the mother of Young God in a trembling voice.

"You hate me, huh?" he said, looking around with his arms wide open to show the luxurious life around him.

"You, your arrogance, your ego, your narcissism, your selfishness, your greed, your insatiable desire to rule. You, your disgusting friends, putting yourselves in place of God..."

"You know, you always make the same big mistake! Your father, although your whole family is one of us, you never wanted to understand or accept. You failed to learn. We don't put ourselves in God's place; WE ARE GOD. And we can play any game we want with these stupid people, with their lives, their destinies."

"You are sick, all of you!"

"No, not me; you are sick. You are a *sick born* person with unnecessary emotionality, the sensitivity of irritability, and maladaptive, asocial, depressive, mental health conditions. And no matter what I've done, you made my son, my only heir, like yourself too. But I don't want to put up with you and your diseases anymore while all these stupid people, the world, have transformed into how I want," he said.

And with that, he stabbed the sharp steak knife in his hand into his wife's throat, as she sat next to him.

Young God was only fourteen years old when his father took him on a world tour to develop his ability to rule. And he was only fourteen years old when his father forced him to watch as a soldier of one of their tribal chiefs cut off the head of a rebellious young boy. Eleven years had passed since the blood from the young man's throat had gushed onto the Young God's face. For eleven years the Young God had been living with these memories. He remembered how the boy bellowed like a tortured animal, the trembling of his legs and arms even minutes after his head was cut off, the little jumps in the air, the terrifying painful look of the eyes on the severed head. It was eleven years since he met the bottomless look in the eyes of the soldiers and the monstrosity of his father, who watched them smiling and proud.

And now he was only twenty-five years old and his heart had been ripped out by a woman who had lost her soul to power and money. His unborn child and his wife had been murdered by his father. This Young God, whose name is Daniel, was only twenty-five years old when all this happened. He was forced to kneel by his father beside the bloody dead body of his mother and had been made to swear that he would be under his command in the new world order his father would establish.

Daniel understood his father that day when he knelt before his mother's body. And he accepted it. His father was a God who ruled the world; those around him were Gods. And only Gods could change the world. In whatever way they wanted.

Daniel had understood and accepted that day; he was a God, like them.

And he could change the world.

When the time came...

And when that day came, another twenty years had passed for Daniel, and his seven warriors across seven continents, whose names were Louise, Angela, Carla, Keilee, Marcella, Alessia, and Dustin.

They had to prepare and wait for twenty years to disrupt the murderous world established by the Gods and to start their war.

Twenty long and painful years.

And during these twenty years, the Gods kept on whispering; the world got worse day by day.

The death of Daniel's mother was reflected on the screen as a heart attack, of a woman who could not stand her child's pain. Daniel began to work as his father's right-hand man, his chief soldier, just as his father wanted, from that day on. He started his career as a weapons engineer. He had to be patient until he could become chairperson of the board of directors, of those innumerable companies that make the world a crueller and more murderous place with each passing day.

At his father's order, Daniel married a daughter of the Gods' Floor in a few months to become a "completed person". Daniel and his new wife seemed very happy, and they soon had a son. Daniel took a happy picture of his small family. With that happy family pose, Daniel proved that he had come back to life, had fallen in love again, was a strong person, had moved on with his life, and turned into a completed person. That happy family pose whispered to people that anything could happen in life, but it has to move on no matter what. With this photo and the whispers of the Gods, those who were killing themselves in the streets with the pain they had suffered as 'I am a hunted', those who protested for them, for those who suffered from love, slowly began to return to their homes. Then it began to be voiced that these suicides were unwarranted, that everyone suffered from love many times in life, and that solving it this way was actually a deficiency, a psychological problem. People made fun of the hunted and became insensitive to them.

While these were whispers, news of a man dying of hunger in his manor house, where he lived alone, began to circulate on the screens. The images of this man, who fired all his employees from the house, bankrupted his businesses and imprisoned himself in his house, dried out from hunger and thirst, his thinning skin and his ossified body hit people's faces like a colossal wave. At the bedside of this man, Brone, who appeared to have killed himself slowly and painfully by starving himself for weeks after locking himself in his manor house, a note was found: "I'm hungry. I'm hungry for love! It is impossible to endure the emptiness and pain created by this hunger. This is not being hungry. This is *hunger*." Brone, who was dumped a year ago by his girlfriend, whom he was madly in love with, who tried every way to win her back, going to her door for months and begging her on his knees, went down in history as the first known *'hunger'*.

And a new word has been added to the dictionary: *'Hungers'*.

Hunger(s): People who feel depressed by thinking that no one is in love with them feel hunger for love by falling into deep emotional emptiness. These people, who are overly emotional, touchy, incompatible and asocial, always feel incomplete regardless of their financial income, career, education and social opportunities due to severe depressive mental disorders and mental illnesses. Due to their deep depression, they are generally suicidal and often cannot be saved despite all interventions. Because of their emotional hunger they condemn themselves to hunger in real life. Those people are called 'hungers'.

When *hungers* was first defined, people tried to understand what this definition meant. Some people felt Brone's pain in their hearts, but as the number of people who mocked and humiliated the hungers increased day by day, they too fell silent. It was a lack of coping with an ordinary life issue. While people played the game of three monkeys with this disease, they did not know or could not see that this disease was connected with *'hunters'* and *'hunted'*.

But they would understand with the Gods' whispers.

They would understand in the new world of Gods.

In the days that followed, as people started to forget the death of the first hunger, a video of a beggar began to circulate on all the communication networks. On his knees and pleading to people, this man was not begging for money, bread, a hot bowl of soup, food, or shelter. This man was begging people for love! "Isn't there a warm heart to love me? Is there no one to hug me? A pair of warm arms! A shoulder to lean on! I beg you!"

And so the world met the first *'Beggar of Love'*.

People were surprised at first by this situation; they had never encountered such a thing before. Then some people stood in front of him and watched with laughter, while others looked at him with pity and opened their arms. As the days passed, others began to appear alongside this man. "Hug me! I'm about to die of lovelessness! I beg you!" The number of beggars of love, who opened their hands in supplication, increased, as did the number of people who stood before them laughing, or looked at them with pity, or embraced them. The pitying attention of the whole world had turned to them.

A few weeks later, the first known *Beggar of Love* was a guest on a television show. Though hundreds of people had surrounded him for weeks, he still had a bottomless, deep dark look in his eyes instead of a glimmer of hope. The announcer said to him,

"Lennon, you started a very different trend. All over the world, on the pavements, people began to open their palms for love boldly, and someone hugged them. It's amazing how people connected in this way. Still, I have to ask as we have a lot of viewers wondering. You know, we've all had heartbreak. Your financial means, career and social environment are perfect. Is it a fact or a psychological condition that you think no one is in love with you? Even though you don't lock yourself up in your house and torture yourself with real hunger, aren't you just a different version of the hungers?"

"No one loved me! Never once in my life have I actually heard the sentence 'I love you' from anyone. Only those who stand in front of the mirror and ask the bitter question, 'Why hasn't anyone fallen in love with me?' can understand what this means. There are more people than you can imagine who ask this question when they're alone, but no one can say it frankly, because it's a big shame if no one has ever fallen in love with you. I'm a hunger yes, to a pair of loving eyes, to stares!"

The announcer looked at Lennon with puzzled and pitying eyes, "Yes, Lennon, you cannot believe the wind and chain of love you have created in the world. On the one hand, the beggars of love come out bravely and extend their hands; on the other hand, people feed them with their love. Thanks to this chain of love formed worldwide, it was decided to establish 'The Beggars of Love Centres' in different countries. By sending a message to the number that appears on the screen, you can establish these centres by paying only 2 pounds. Although you cannot come here and hug Lennon, you can convey your tolerance and understanding to him and others like him. Remember, it's only 2 pounds. You don't have to think much for that money that's an unnecessary weight in the corner of your wallet. Let's help these people together. I guess that's great news for all the beggars of love. What do you say, Lennon?"

"Only two pounds," said Lennon and fell silent.

"Yes, I love it when everyone pulls together to help – the simplest and most effective organization in the world. Lennon, I'm sure you'll be full of love at these centres."

"You're right. Just two pounds could do anything, couldn't it? You could feed the starving, drill water wells and fight drought, build houses for the homeless in disaster areas and big cities, open addiction centres. It could go on and on. You can put all the pain you don't want to see in the world in a jar and close the lid with that two pounds, that unwanted weight in your wallet. You can ease your conscience about all these things in this simple way.

"But you cannot fill the hunger for love or massive gap in their hearts and souls in people with two pounds. You cannot cure them with two pounds.

"Will you donate two pounds of love? How could two pounds of love be donated? Do you have a method for it?
"Will the staff hug me with a dose of two pounds

three times a day in that centre? Will they give me two pounds of love gazes three times a day?

"Is this how it will be?

"You can't give me love with two pounds; you can't offer me your love when you hug me while I open my hand in the street and beg. The only thing you can feel is that of 'pity'. And while I struggle with this hunger for love, the pity in your gaze, in your arms, becomes nothing but a whirlpool that quickly pulls me to the bottom. Do not pity me, do not pity us. I don't need your two-pounds pity," he shouted.

The announcer was stunned, he didn't know what to say, but he had an expert director and whispered in his ear, "Yes, they will treat you in the centres that will be set up with those two-pound donations. Because you all are hunger and you need intensive treatment."

"Hungers are not sick people. It is not a disease to be emotional, to be sensitive," Lennon began to shout, getting up.

The director interrupted the broadcast at that moment, and adverts appeared on the screen. Seeing the security guards approaching him, Lennon swung his chair around, ran out of the studio, and escaped.

When he went back to the spot where he begged, all the people who wanted to hug him had disappeared. Because the Gods had whispered again, and whispers moved faster than anything else in the world. People were passing them by, making fun or looking at the beggars with disgust after that day. And they were sitting there, with empty, aimless, meaningless eyes, in dead silence too. The days went by like this. *The beggars of love* had stayed where they were, hungry, thirsty, motionless, their dark eyes filled with pain, their bodies collapsing more and more each day. Rain and snow fell on them; winds blew, people passed by them every day, disgust in their gaze.

But the worst was yet to come. The Gods had the final trick up their sleeve. The day would come. The day that would go down in history as 'Bloody Beggar' Day. And after that everyone would start to exclude them, to fear them.

At first, however, the definition of hunger was expanded:

The hungers turn into the beggars of love over time. Although they only harmed themselves when they first appeared, they later started to attack others. It has been determined that the hungers who do not attempt attacks on others nevertheless disrupt the peace of society due to their constant jealous and depressive actions. Since they emerged, many hungers have been caught trying to turn those around like themselves with their depression and irritability. The hungers and the beggars of love, who come under the most dangerous mental illness category, need special treatment in hospital.

The Gods had come to the most fun part of the cascading psychological transition they had started, as they moved towards their endgame.

As the definitions expanded, the Gods, who knew that they brought out the evils in people so easily, added the term 'Sick born' to the dictionary. The hunted, the hungers, the beggars of love were no longer just seriously ill and in need of treatment but were labelled congenitally 'sick born' people. They were ill people who were born with this illness. People were told to report the hungers and beggars of love on sight for hospitalization.

Thus the Gods had reached the final stage in their new world order game.

The Gods first taught people the 'art of being happy', how to get rid of unnecessary people in their lives, deal with daily and ordinary problems, start each day with a smile, and always appear strong. Seminars and conferences were organized, movies played, songs sang, books written, and influencers created.

Humans are creatures that quickly adapt to anything. As the people disgraced by these teachings of the Gods began to be excluded, the last point was added to the dictionary:
Those who live alone regardless of their education, culture, career and financial level, those who do not have at least six friends around on their special days, stay alone after work or on weekends, who cannot find a group of friends during their holidays are actually a hunger.

And with this final definition, the amusing

psychological game-building phase for the Gods was over. Before starting the real game, the Gods stepped aside and watched how people would trap and cause each other to be killed before announcing their new world. They knew people well. They knew best what people would do to stay alive; also their greed, ego, jealousy, desire for money and power.

From that day on, people became afraid of looking unhappy or sad, of crying or being sensitive when they felt bad. As in every period of history, some people adapted very quickly to the new order. *Manipulators! Manipulators who wanted to rise rapidly in the workplace and remove the obstacles in front of them started to play with the psychology of their competitors.* And with each passing day, someone would seek to trap someone else by extending their index finger and saying, "He/she is a hunger", and simply remove any obstacles on the career ladder.

While manipulators were multiplying rapidly in the business world, *hookers* began to appear – trapping wealthy people with their *barbed hooks. The hookers were those who followed in the footsteps of Nancy. Her heirs. They ensured their comfortable lives by marrying the lonely people or amassing big groups of friends for such people. Those they trapped could not speak out for fear of being declared a hunger and had to endure the increasingly ugly tricks of the hookers.*

So, with each passing day, more and more beggars of love and hungers began to fall onto the streets. Those who were not financially able to play this game, those who could not keep up with the humiliating, sadistic rules of the hookers, or who could not resist the manipulators' plays. Unhappy with their presence, the people demanded that these beggars be cleared from the streets. The Gods did not refuse their request, and one morning the first 'beggar tunnel' was opened at one end of the largest park in the centre of the city.

And with this tunnel, the Gods commenced the real game.

First, beggar tunnels were opened all over the world. Then they planted robot soldiers and robot dogs on the streets and at the entrances to the tunnels. They placed agents in shopping centres, workplaces, parks, schools, hospitals, inside families.

It took about five years for people to get used to this situation. For the first five years, hundreds of people were declared hungers and beggars of love every day and sent to these tunnels. Thereafter, people learned how to behave among the hunters and hookers. In other words, they learned always to appear strong, happy and always smiling.

But that wasn't easy.
And they failed… Millions of them…

But no one could show or express their unhappiness. They were afraid of being thrown into those tunnels as a hunger or beggar of love or forced to surrender and go to those tunnels independently. And all those ever strong, ever happy, ever smiling bodies were filled with a bottomless sadness.

Then one day, to the people's surprise, the Gods decided to reduce working hours and increase salaries for happier and more productive members of society. Working hours changed, from 10 am to 4 pm. Fridays were also included in the weekend break. Annual break periods were extended. The people first rejoiced at this and thanked their Gods. But those who did not have a wide circle of friends and an active social life and could not prove this in their social media posts understood the meaning of these rules quickly. An endless playground was opened up for hookers and hunters. As lonely people got richer and had more time to socialize, they had to cooperate with hookers, give them all the money they earned and create fake friendships, social environments, loves and marriages.

So why did the Gods play such a game? Why did they want such a new world order?

Daniel had asked the same question in the very first days too. And as a God, it did not take long for him to find the answer.

The Gods had managed to manipulate and desensitize people in developed countries with their games for centuries, but they still could not silence those rebellious voices that were heard in between. They hated people's sensibilities.

They could not understand how Van Gogh and artists like him continued to produce their works despite their lives of misery and psychological trauma. They were jealous of their determination and the beautiful works they produced.

The Gods were disgusted with people power that arose among those born and raised in countries where the weapons they produced in their factories for centuries had caused so much hunger, drought, war and misery. Despite their terrible living conditions, they were still able to laugh, fall in love, and be happy. So for that the Gods hated them.

Because the Gods, although they ruled the world, owned the world, and had been able to take everything from people for many thousands of years, had not been able to smile like the children struggling in that hell, not even once, with that bottomless insatiability within.

They understood that they had nothing good to leave to people, not like the artists who cling to life despite their lives spent in poverty, pain and psychological traumas.

Because the Gods were not human: instead of blood, the poison of power and ego flowed in their veins. That's why they gave the world only hunger, war, famine, envy, enmity, cruelty.

But there came a time when the Gods realized that ordinary people could struggle against anything as long as they were not alone, under any circumstances; and that they could be happy as long as they were not alone, even under the worst conditions. Although they knew that Maslow's Hierarchy of Needs had a mistake, they continued to teach it in schools and raise children by making them believe in it.

And these poisonous Gods had finally discovered the one thing that could take away the happiness from these people who could laugh despite everything: the hunger for love.

In this new world order they established, the Gods produced more drugs in underdeveloped countries through the force of arms, and sold more drugs for the free, prosperous and ever happy people of the developed countries. In this new world order, in these developed countries, there was ugliness and psychological warfare unprecedented in history that no one could stand. So they used more drugs to stay alive, to manage to play those games; and the Gods gained more money, ego and power.

In this new world order that the Gods established, they caused more brutal wars, famines, and disasters with the weapons they produced and sold. The people of the developed countries, forced to be ever happy, always smiling, could not care about what was going on, on the other side of the world; they only had to watch it from this dungeon of happiness.

There was no longer a single person in the streets who sought to raise their voice against the evil in the world. The Gods had played their greatest, most potent game ever, and the humans had finally kneeled down in obeisance and held out their palms. And the Gods were overjoyed with this game of unbearable pain.

Daniel was only twenty-five years old when all this began. During the intervening twenty years, he watched what was happening: the unhappiness of the people, his own unhappiness, and the unhappiness of the Gods.

Daniel was only twenty-five years old when his father forced him to kneel at his mother's bloody body and he made that great vow in his heart.

And for twenty years, he spent every moment remembering that day, his promise of revenge to his mother, to his unborn baby, and himself.

Daniel spent his life reminding himself that he did not want to be a God in such a world, that he was not one of them, but that only a God could disrupt the toxic world order forged by these poisonous Gods.

And he was a God.

IT WILL ALWAYS BE YOU

Saturday, July 10, 2021

It was one minute past twelve midnight on Saturday, July 10, 2021. I was waiting for an Uber outside Gatwick Airport with a large suitcase and a handbag. I had returned from Turkey eleven days ago. As Turkey was on the red list due to the coronavirus, I had to pay £1750 pounds and stay in quarantine for ten days at the Sofitel Hotel near the airport.

When I got into the Uber, I opened the window and breathed the air that hit my face during the journey as the driver was driving along the dark motorway at full speed.

Fresh air! Oxygen!

During the quarantine period, as we were confined to a room for ten days in that damn disgusting hotel and had only been allowed a fifteen minute breather each day, all I needed at that moment was fresh air. Although I had arrived in England at Heathrow Airport on the evening of 29 June, they took me to a hotel near Gatwick. Thus, after three years, I had stepped into England again, by a strange coincidence, on 10 July.

The dates were the same, but not a single thing in my life had remained the same.

Most importantly, exactly three years after 10 July 2018, I was walking the streets of London as a free woman on the same day. Yes, I was finally divorced!

X found himself a 'sugar mum', trusted her and accepted the divorce, and I completely got rid of that leech.

My arrival on July 10 didn't happen by going through passport control at the airport like the first time. I was in England without being able to touch or breathe it, just having to look out at it. I had taken that first step by spending ten days where I had to stop still, before completing the last missing part of the Dilek I wanted to be.

England took me by the arms and shook me with all its might over those ten days. In 3 Hilsea Street, I had locked myself in that box room and shook off even the smallest piece of my soul from all the psychological deficiencies, evils, problems and fears that I had purged from myself while I was writing my book. And this quarantine, staying ten days in silence, was preparing me for my real loneliness. There was a life I wanted to build for myself in England, and the first step I had to take fearlessly on the path to this life was to meet my loneliness as the new Dilek I created.

And I opened the door of my new home with this key of loneliness.

What was the life I wanted to build in England? What had happened in 3 Hilsea Street that I wanted to drag myself into such loneliness? What had happened to those angels, that wonderful, enviable friendship, and why had I moved from 3 Hilsea Street?

Nothing had happened.

Just lockdown was over.

Only I had purged myself of all my psychological problems and was no longer afraid of anything. Even though I was alone and in a difficult situation as a woman in England, I had not trapped myself in the transparent bubble of the Turkish-speaking community. I would not squeeze the new Dilek into 3 Hilsea Street, and I would not be afraid to take bigger steps. With this power, I would first meet real loneliness and then move on with my real friends in England who would stay in my life.

Real loneliness! True friendship! True Dilek! The real-life I wanted to build!

Did I lie about my housemates, 3 Hilsea Street, X, what had happened in my life, and of course, my love affair with Bobby? Were those 442 pages I wrote my true story, or did I actually write a novel – a work of fiction perhaps?

No, I didn't lie, not a single word.

I just softened it a lot, exaggerated it a bit, showed it the way it should be, and added colour.

Because when I locked myself in my room and finished the first draft of the book in a single week, without sleeping day or night, and read what I had written, I was horrified. When I closed myself up in my room and started to write, and while the first draft was being created, I was still the severely injured Dilek. After I read in those lines what I'd been through in that hell for the last six years, I didn't want to believe it, went to the bathroom and vomited until only bitter bile came up from my empty stomach. I lost my self-confidence for a few days. I hated everyone and everything. What I went through, what I wrote was very heavy.

I did not want to create myself in those lines or make people read such heaviness. I asked myself, "What do I want to tell people? Did I mean to say, by crying, whining, about what I have suffered in my life: 'look, read and get down like me' or 'understand my wounds, have pity on me, hug me with pity'?"

No, never. That was not what I wanted to say.

I first tried to show women, and everyone else, that no matter how bad the people who come into your life, you can find a way to escape the dire situation you are in, no matter the circumstances. You might encounter psychological trauma, fear and depression, innumerable times, until the way out is found. You could roll over, and your body be covered in blood. You could crawl, make a thousand mistakes, take wrong ways. In the process, people you trust may turn their backs on you, and you could be alone. You could turn into a hunger! With the hunger for love and understanding, which is the most dangerous psychological void you could tumble into, you could bring the wrong people into your life, become addicted to drugs or alcohol, and fall into the clutches of mental illness.

When you tried to get among people, the loneliness you fell into could have taken you from your environment and pulled you into the darkness. While you were struggling with your problems in your own darkness, people might not tolerate you, treat you with disdain, exclude you, calling you 'sick born'.

The silence in your solitude could be an adjective and became a literal description of your situation, or the silence could be a verb that could kill you.

It might have killed me too.

Silence and all those negative emotions... A few nights before I locked myself in my room and started writing, I had acted in collusion with all those negative emotions while taking my anger off my walls and let those emotions take me over completely. Instead of holding on to our good times, I had only chosen to see how people hurt me.

If the book had remained as it was, it could have been a masterpiece of the dark literary world. But I didn't want to call out to the darkness; I didn't want people to pity me. It was a bad period of my life. I did not want either that terrible time or my pain to humiliate my words. I didn't want people reading my book to do that in their own lives.

So, I decided to change what I had written entirely. Doing something I would never do, I deleted that draft from my computer, fearing the darkness of that book, without making a single copy. I left my room, took a bath, put on clean clothes, and went down to the kitchen. Giulia was cooking at the time.

Having not seen me for days, when I entered the kitchen, she opened her arms and said "Ciao Piccolina" and gave me a huge hug with her usual beaming smile. I hugged her back, more tightly than ever. By a pleasing coincidence, that evening, all the residents of the house were in the kitchen. We ate our meal together, teased each other, chatted, laughed, watched *Peep Show* for a while, parroting the lines we had memorized over many previous evenings, and then dispersed to our rooms.

Just like in my first book, it was a typical Hilsea Street evening. But neither that evening nor the previous evenings at No. 3 were perfect.

None of us was.

Because we were human, and none of us was perfect or an angel.

Accepting it that evening, when I locked myself in my room again, instead of getting stuck in that dark book, stuck in the flaws, drowning in pain and falling into the darkness, I started to write those lines towards hope, friendship and love. No matter how much pain it contains.

So what was the real story?

All my experiences with X were real, only a very, very small part of what happened, and I softened a lot of what happened as I told my tale.

I didn't mention almost any of my bad experiences with the Turkish community in England.

To add some sex appeal to the book, I made up the stories of intimacy with those three imaginary men when I worked in the boutique in Nothing Hill. Before I came to England, I was incapable of touching anyone. I felt nothing but distrust and repulsion of men due to my experiences with X. I would instantly turn my face away in disgust if someone looked at me. Right after I set foot in England, nor could I ever touch anyone else because of my dreams, the energy that surrounded my heart with that blue paint stained finger. I tried many times, but I couldn't.

3 Hilsea Street was real. But we were human, and, only naturally, we would encounter some problems in between. However, while I was writing, I rubbed any rankling away and turned them into angels, entirely, and turned the only troubled person into me.

Yes, from the first day I stepped into that house, I felt safe; safe enough to sleep without locking my broken door. Yes, almost every Sunday, Stephen and Matt would prepare a traditional English breakfast and Sunday roasts for us all. We played card games, scrabble, darts. Some Fridays or weekends we had barbecue parties, sometimes some of us cooked our traditional food and sat at the table together in the evenings. We had parties in the kitchen or Jeff's room almost every Friday or Saturday evening, got very drunk, conjured up unthinkable oddities, craziness, fun. We laughed a lot, had a lot of lively, happy times.

Yes, some evenings, I got drunk at those parties with my friends; I cried in their arms because I longed for Bobby. But I only talked about Bobby for the first few weeks until they got fed up with me. After Agata said to me one day, "Everyone suffers from love. Don't be a drama queen," I couldn't talk about it easily with anyone other than Giulia. My housemates had only witnessed me texting Bobby dozens and dozens of lines of messages. Although they didn't know what I was writing, I stopped texting when I was in their company after a while because they were alarmed by the length of those messages. But Bobby…

Yes, there were times when I suffered psychological breakdown and behaved in strange and crazy ways due to all my problems. X's ongoing harassment, and the never approaching divorce. But most of the time, I didn't reflect on these at 3 Hilsea Street. On the contrary, I was smiling, cheerful and even more energetic than them most of the time. As I described in my first book, I did not pass out by drinking all day and all night. I did not drink alcohol separately from them. I only drank at the parties or evening gatherings. Amid all these struggles, I only went to the Turkish shop twice and yes, I bought a bottle of raki and finished that raki by myself. But it wasn't because I was an alcoholic or looking for solutions to my problems with drink. I drank that raki because actually it's a very traditional Turkish thing to do for those who suffer from love. My housemates didn't join me because they found the raki too heavy.

If I were in Turkey or with one of my friends from there in England, they would have joined me, and that raki table would have become what we call the 'locksmith's table'. We would have eaten our traditional food; we would have listened to the most depressing Turkish traditional music and cried along with those songs. Then I would have sent a few hundred more messages to the man who was making me suffer from love. I would have gone through a thousand feelings simultaneously and gone to sleep completely drunk. Then I would have woken up the following day with undoubtedly a thumping headache, end the day with a hangover, and maybe then completely relax. The 'locksmith's table' would have done its job; that is, it would have allowed me to pour out the pain within me and relax. But there was no one here to accompany me.

So it was only on two occasions when I felt most depressed, that I sat alone in the garden and listened to the darkest Turkish music on my earphones, and sometimes accompanied their refrains with whispers, with tears flowing down my cheeks from time to time. I drank silently, caressing Otto the cat, who was the only being I described in my book without altering anything, and who would come onto my lap and comfort me whenever I needed it. I mean, I didn't cause a single inconvenience to the people in the house. But to Bobby...

Yes, I didn't eat for a very long time. Everyone in the house kindly warned me to take care of myself, sharing their meals with me from time to time. But they never did anything like forcefully put food in my mouth. As an adult, I did not expect such a thing from them. Although I did not eat until I was close to dying from starvation, I did not want to die, so I stuck something in my stomach at the most critical moments and continued to survive.

Yes, after seeing Bobby for the second time, I was in bed for days with a fever of forty-two degrees with sadness. Agatha didn't make me soup – she didn't even ask; she would never have asked either, She was the only person in the house who didn't share her food. The guys didn't knock on my door to see if I was alive or dead; they didn't even understand I was sick. And my little sunshine Giulia didn't make me herbal tea either. She was at her boyfriend's over the time I was ill. But Bobby…

And after my illness, I realized one more time and had to accept the fact that as long as I went into the kitchen with my big smile and powerful energy, I would be a friend. Otherwise, I would be the drama queen, as far as they were concerned, and they wouldn't want to have much to do with me or be my friend. So, I had to always show 'my good side'.

Yes, I had claustrophobia, I had a fear of loss; I fought those stone soldiers, the ants, and I inscribed crazy things on the walls of my room. But no one knew about it, except for Giulia, who eventually came to my room wondering how I was. And of course, Bobby… I never bothered anyone until I painted the walls of my room with that foul smelling paint. And because I explained that I had made the mistake of using that paint, thinking that that smell would go away after airing the room, no one said anything. After that insane night in my room, I started the day after getting rid of everything and as if nothing had happened the night before, and I had celebrated the Halloween party by drinking water.

Yes, I had to sleep in that leather armchair in the kitchen until that nasty smell in my room dissipated. No one suggested that I could sleep in their room, except for Jeff, who had a sofa in his room, but I didn't go. If any of the others had asked me, I would have declined because I knew I had to stay in the kitchen with Otto.

At the end of those four days, I locked myself in my room and started writing.

And until that day came, unlike the miserable state I describe in the book, I acted as strong, happy, smiling, energetic among my friends. I made fun of my slowly improving English, my mistakes, my flaws before them. I was starting a new life in a new country. They smiled and hugged me the first day I came home, and I returned that love tenfold, understanding friendship.

From the day I stepped into the house, I would tidy up and clean the common areas, the kitchen, bathroom and stairs by myself, ignoring Agatha's constant comments that I was being 'being stupid' to do so, as there was a cleaning rota. Except when I wasn't truly depressed, the kitchen counter or bathroom was never dirty, until I locked myself in the room to write the book. After getting used to a new home and kitchen, I occasionally made appetizers, traditional Turkish dishes, vitamin bomb soups, but mostly pastry-style cookies and cakes. When I ate, from the first meal I made to the very last meal in that house, if there was someone around, I would always invite them to share my food. Perhaps it was strange behaviour for people who were just housemates, all with their individual lives, but I knew that I was living among nice people, and I knew that kindness could spread among good people. So everyone was asked or offered to share their own meals. When the kitchen shelves were allocated to me, from the very first day I arrived, I said to them, "You don't need to ask, get whatever you need from my shelf", and I joined them in generosity.

So why did I reflect myself as being in a much worse psychological state than I was and turn the inhabitants at 3 Hilsea Street into angels, in a book that will exist forever?

I wanted to instil hope in people that such beautiful, unprejudiced, disinterested friendships still exist in the world. I described how house sharing, companionship, friendship should be like in the first book. The concepts of love, understanding, compassion, interest, friendship had to replace the real viruses that swept the world – loneliness, lovelessness, jealousy, envy, hatred, enmity... And there could not be a more beautiful roof in London than No. 3 Hilsea Street, host and home to people from many different countries of the world.

Although I wasn't destroyed in real life for months on

end, I had to completely collapse and get back on my feet in the book's story to set an example for people. Because with the condition I was in and my life full of problems, I could have well been in as bad a situation as I described in my book, or even worse. I could have really become an alcoholic. I could have used drugs. Apart from my claustrophobia and fear of loss, I could have fallen prey to mental illness and depression and be faced with psychological problems and the need for medication. But I've never done anything to myself, except for a few serious falls.

Even though we had our problems, good people had come into my life. Knowing that we are all struggling with all our issues, I always chose to hold onto their good side, the clean side of their hearts. While hugging them, I would say a million times, "I'm so lucky to have friends like you". Despite all the negativities, I did consider myself very lucky. I had a talent, and I knew that by holding onto that talent, my words, and hoping, I could manage to come back from the brink of depression, moreover, by completely curing myself, purifying, re-creating myself even more strongly. But Bobby…

Yes, I saved myself, treated and purged myself as the words poured from my fingers and turned into an entirely different Dilek. After that, I tried to say something to people who had problems themselves and were trying to find a way to save themselves: "You can be stuck to shit in your life, but no worries. You can find a drop of clean water to clean yourself, a dirty puddle, a handful of sand, or a rock to rub it off on. If you can't find those, let the shit on you dry up. The sun will hit you as you continue on, and that shit will dry and fall off bit by bit. Its smell will stay on you for a long time, but as you continue on your way and keep walking, that smell will go away with the rain and wind. Lean your soul against the little beauties life offers you and keep walking, instead of looking at the shit on you and denying yourself."

So, what about our reality, Bobby and me?

Maybe you were waiting for would happen next when you read the last lines of the first book, and probably you didn't believe it was true. Maybe you asked as you started this book, and are asking now as you read these lines, "So where is Bobby?" Was what I went through with him real? Or did I exaggerate and turn it into such a miraculous love to give hope that there is still powerful supernatural love in the world?

No.

Putting up with my madness, seeing, reading, trying to understand, and answering, were all on Bobby's shoulders all through this story.

That nightmare I had in 2014, that tiger that illuminated my path, that blue stained finger that came into my dreams afterwards, those feelings that engulfed me, my hallucinations, were all real. And after I set foot in England, I tried for months not to go crazy under the weight of these unrealities among the many real problems. In a strange twist of fate, when X himself gave Bobby to me by swiping right on Tinder, when Bobby started calling me, from the moment he started talking to me, I wandered on the verge of insanity for days because those surrealities had turned into reality. I was lost in that magical love and that Bobby accepted me with all my crazy messages over the 51 days that passed until I moved out of the house where I had to live with X.

That first night, when we lost ourselves in that very first moment we saw each other, and our hands touched, a baby, the baby of our love, fell into my womb with that magical love. And that baby started to grow with my longing for Bobby as the days went by.

Until Bobby accepted those unbelievable feelings and texted me again, my silence was spent touching that baby who was growing word by word in my womb. During our second date, instead of having sex, we spent the whole time hugging, just kissing, smelling and looking at each other with tenderness. That night was proof that we had crushed each other with these strange feelings. When I returned home, that baby who was growing calmly, word by word, suddenly came to life and started kicking. As that baby quickly grew and kicked my belly in excitement and impatience to be born, I wrote Bobby more, longer, more complex, more freaky messages every day, every seconds.

Bobby, who initially tried to reply to my messages, fell silent after a while, not knowing what to do or how to respond. As Bobby went silent, words began to multiply in my womb, and that rapidly growing baby began to shake and kick my belly harder to get out, destroyed my spirit and played with my hormones. Every day I turned on my computer and tried to type, but although it shook me ever more violently, the baby was not yet ready to be born. No matter what I tried, it could not flow out onto the white pages on the computer.

There were two lies in my story about Bobby. The first lie about Bobby was when I started begging him to block me. In the reality- just a few days after our second meeting -in August-, I started pleading with Bobby to block me. Every day, time after time... But no matter what I did, he couldn't stop me, and he was getting quieter and quieter with each passing day. In the end, after a few days our second dates I blocked him on WhatsApp, deleted his number and tried to write on the computer. But I couldn't. That baby was choosing to talk to his father instead, with the endless messages I sent to him.

I wasn't able to understand what the baby was waiting for, what it needed to be born, until the third and last time I saw Bobby. I couldn't understand until he said to me, "I love you", looked me in the eyes with his endless love, but with fears as big and intense as his love, and said, "This can't be real".

After that day, the baby calmed down for a while, and as the day of its birth approached, as Bobby became quiet again with his fears, the baby became more irritable, heavier, and shook my body and soul more vigorously. As the baby was doing this to me, I wrote strange messages to Bobby that no one could bear. Yes, Bobby was silent most of the time, not responding to my texts because I wasn't actually typing messages that could be replied to. They were lines that talked about something but it wasn't really clear what they were about, piecemeal, lengthy, and insane enough to have me admitted to a mental institution. Anyone else in Bobby's place would certainly have had me committed, but he didn't.

Sometimes he tried to calm me down, and sometimes he just couldn't stand it and got angry. "You are right", I would tell him. "You need to get rid of my messages. You must save me from writing to you. Block me from everywhere. You know that if I block you, I will only unblock you and continue to write to you. Block me, let this torture end for both of us." But no matter how hard I begged, he didn't block me. While he couldn't do it, as he read my crazy messages and sometimes laughed and sometimes got angry, that baby kept growing inside me with enthusiasm and excitement.

I did not expect or want anything from him anyway - except to block me- until the day when the baby was ready to be born. In fact, I was in labour pains when I lost my mind, packed my belongings and sent those messages that I repeated a million times, saying, "I'm ready, take me home," as if to prove that I was really crazy. Without asking or knowing where he was or what he was doing. That day, when Bobby called me back after the funeral, and those things had happened between us, the baby's threshold burst, and its tiny head was starting to appear between my legs.

But it still couldn't be born.

The night I scribbled on the walls of my room, I didn't know where to throw myself with all the pain of childbirth. I was texting Bobby about killing myself, then texting that I was fine, just getting drunk, and scaring him again in my following text. As he apologized to me dozens of times for what he had said me, tried to calm me down. I told him that all he had to do to be okay was to stop me. I was pleading with him, "Understand me. You are a person who knows how to live by holding on to your colours. What it means to you to touch those brushes and colours and painting is the same as writing for me. I won't be able to do this unless you block me." He couldn't accept breaking the bond with me and just tried to calm me down, instead of blocking me. Since he didn't do this, I was writhing in pain and did not leave a single space to write anything more on the walls of my room, even on the window sill. As the baby emerged between my legs, those lines changed the colour of the walls, and I was relieved. When Bobby's hand took my heart and placed it between his heart, the baby was born and appeared in my arms.

I had started the following morning with a baby in my arms and a Bobby that I was driving crazy with fear. Nevertheless, I had given birth and I relaxed. So I finished that crazy Halloween party only drinking water. After that lunatic night, Bobby still kept texting me. With a massive hole in my heart, a baby in my arms, and Otto on my lap, as I stared at the computer screen, I only thought about how Bobby would block me while I had to spend four days in the kitchen because of the disgusting paint smell in my room. Even though I sent him those last unacceptable messages, he still didn't block me. It was the second and last lie in my story with Bobby. Even though I sent him those disgusting messages, he didn't block me like I described in the first book because of those messages.

After I returned to my room and stared at the computer screen, I finally discovered what I had to do. When we started texting again before our second meeting, the sentence he wrote to me, "I can't bear it if you are touching anyone else," came to mind. A few hours into the day after the night I had driven Bobby crazy with fear of my death, I made a short video of photos taken while having fun with my friends at the Halloween party. I knew I would piss him off with a video like this just a day after driving him to distraction with text messages saying I would kill myself. And in that video, I added the photos that we all took together also with Manuel, cuddling, smelling of love, and creating the air of kissing. Bobby didn't know Manuel was gay, that we took the photos just for fun.

And he got furious because he didn't know.

Seconds after I sent him that video, those text bubbles first moved, flashed for minutes with anger, resentment, and of course, intense disappointment. Then they stopped. And then Bobby's picture on WhatsApp disappeared.

He had blocked me.

Not from four months of pleading, thousands of lines of crazy messages, even insults sometimes… but because of a photograph of me in someone else's arms. Shortly after the picture on WhatsApp disappeared, I checked his social media accounts, and finally, I called, and a voicemail box appeared.

He had blocked me from everywhere.

And that's when I learned what real pain meant. What Bobby's silence meant.

After we met the first time, as he pulled back, terrified of these intense feelings, and stopped texting me over those two months, I thought he was a *'hunter'*.

He had *hunted* me!

I thought, I am a hunger and a beggar of love because of all that has happened in my life. So I went to the beggar tunnels. I leant my back against the walls of the beggar tunnels and watched those maggots crawling over my body to eat me alive. And the book *The Beggars of Love* started to appear like a blood clot in my womb.

On our second meeting, a few days after he began to fall into silence with his fears again, I said to him, "You may not want to see me again, talk or text me. I can deal with all of that. Just tell me you don't want it and then block me. As you sink into that deep silence, I will try to fill that bottomless void with thousands of words and continue to send you endless messages."

But since Bobby didn't do what I said, Daniel came to me as I filled that silence with those messages and watched the maggots crawling on my body in those beggar tunnels and nibble at my flesh.

Daniel told me, "He is not a hunter. You created the Hunters, but you don't quite know what it means yet. You created our world, but you don't quite know what's going on in it yet. I am the first baby carried in your womb, but I am not the first child you have to give birth to." He extended his hand and led me out of the beggar tunnels.

Until I saw Bobby for the third and last time, I continued to question what his silence meant. Until that day, I thought that all this was a trick of my brain. The people around me were right, that I was actually obsessed with him. While I was consoling myself with Otto and questioning my obsession, the melodies of those sorrowful songs composed by *Wilbert* in my future book that I *named 'Twelve Songs'* began to fill my ears.

The last time I saw Bobby, and he said to me, "I love you. All this can't be real," I asked him, "I know we can't be together. Why don't you block me and save us both from this madness? Why don't you want to set us free?"

As I asked him, he frowned and shook his head, "I can't!"

After returning from Bobby's house, Wilbert came to me to play his happiest tune, saying, "You know deeply what obsession means, and you're not obsessed with him. Soon you'll find out what Bobby's silence means. I am the second baby who came into your womb, but I am not the first child who has to be born." Then he held my hand and took me to my room.

While I was writing those hundreds of words on my room walls, then spending four days in the kitchen with the baby in my arms, a bleeding emptiness in my heart, and Otto on my lap, Wilbert kept playing his tunes to me. But none of them could tell me what Bobby's silence meant.

Until I found a way for him to block me, and I faced the real meaning of pain.

The moment Bobby blocked me, I had surrendered to the pain of losing him. I started writing as I listened to Wilbert's scorching songs and watched the maggots now eating me alive. I finished the first rough draft of the books The Beggars of Love and Twelve Songs. Then I opened The Beggars of Love file and started writing that book. But Daniel and Wilbert came to me.

Daniel said, "I waited twenty years until the right time came for me, to begin to wage war. If you give birth to us before the first book you are supposed to write, the timing won't be right. You won't be able to understand your dreams, your hallucinations, why and how you met Bobby in this way and the reason for his silence," and he stopped me.

I stopped.

I closed the file of The Beggars of Love, saving what I had written. I started questioning what all this meant and why.

Why?
I kept looking at the two text files on the screen in front of me, and I asked myself:

Why?
I was groaning, sobbing, crying, gasping for breath. Looking at the two text files on the screen in front of me.

Why? I asked.

Daniel and Wilbert sat across from me on the bed, staring at me. My laptop was in front of them, the light from my screen illuminating their faces. They were smiling at me. Slowly I calmed down. I stopped crying. I looked back at them. I swallowed my breath.

I got it.

When I married X, I created a lake of blood for myself. In those six years, that bloody lake overflowed. When I met Bobby, I was struggling to avoid drowning in that bloody lake. When I started texting with him, a sunny, warm, green island appeared off the shore of the lake. When I first tried to climb onto its immaculate, golden sands, I had stepped with blood flowing from my body. So those sands became dirty, and the blood dried on my skin. It prevented me from moving and began to transform me into a statue frozen alive in blood. I threw myself back into the lake in order not to pollute that island and not to turn into a painful, bloody statue on the shore.

Until Daniel and Wilbert pointed me to the story files I had written, I thought those supernatural events before I met Bobby, what I felt when I saw Bobby, that why Bobby came into my life with his fears, his silence, was all so the bloody lake could overflow even more.

Finally, when I realized what all this was, a lightning bolt fell from the dark sky on the roof of that bloody lake into the middle of the lake and turned into a pen. I held onto that pen and made pencil drawings. Then that dark sky began to roar and rain fell unceasingly until the last drop of blood had been washed from the lake and from my body and turned into a pure, clear blue lake. Then the sun came up, and a huge rainbow appeared in the sky and dripped into the lake as colours. The lake, my body, took on a thousand colours, and I started painting with those colours. As I made paintings, words now began to rain from the sky. Thousands of words, covered with colours, mingled with the waters of the lake. Thousands of words, covered with colours, stuck to my skin, wrapped around my body, and flowed into my womb. I made a raft and oars from those words, went to that island beach, and gave birth to four colourful babies. When I took my babies in my arms and looked around, there was a clear lake and a deep blue sky in front of me. I was finally able to go to that heavenly island and its golden yellow sands, coloured with hues that glide from my skin and my babies' skin, making transitions from tone to tone.

And it happened in Bobby's silence.

If he were someone who could mock my crazy messages or think I was mentally ill and truly fear me, he would have blocked me even in those first fifty-one days, long, long before I begged him. And perhaps none of these books would ever have come into the world. But he didn't block me. His existence became that paradise island that I wanted to reach, as a new Dilek. His silence became the sky where my words, which could only create themselves in those messages as I felt his presence, and which overflowed in my mind, took shelter in order not to disappear. That silence hidden, fed, raised, multiplied them. When the right time came, his silence returned my words from the sky with the rains, creating a brand new colourful self inside me.

Once I understood all this, I started to write again. Still, the first draft was dark. But I was no longer in darkness. I was purified, my skin and words were covered with colours, and I gave birth to four babies with those colours. And those babies had to grow up with those colours. After returning to my room, I erased that dark outline and tried to explain what I wanted to tell, and started to write the first book that should have been born. I called it "It is not an immigrant story". Even though I titled my book "It is not an immigrant story", I felt that something was missing from the title. The first night I went to

Turkey, I couldn't sleep as usual. I opened my computer with whispers and completed the book's title: "It is not an immigrant story, It was always you". After that night, when Bobby shared that painting with the words "It was always you" on it, I smiled and thanked that metaphysical connection. Those supernatural powers that continue between us somehow, unwittingly, had led him to create this painting.

In the photo message I sent to Bobby after I published my first two books in Turkey, I explained the bond between me and Manuel and why had I sent him the video. I also said that I had started to write a new book, but I didn't tell him anything about what I was writing. When he posted the song "Mr Writer", in his steamy voice, on Instagram, I felt a little relieved because I understood that the message I had sent him the day before had reached him, and he understood me a little.

On February 7, the book was finished. I had completed it without stopping, in a worse physical condition than I described in the first book. That day, I printed out some pages from the book and translated some paragraphs into English with the help of Google Translate. I included a letter in the translation telling Bobby that I was writing a book about us, that I was going to use his real name and that I was going to use his painting on the cover of the book, and sent the pages to him.

After sending the letter, I slept for three days. My body needed to recover, and my eyes, blinded by constantly staring at the screen, needed to heal. And of course, I had to find a translator to translate my book into English. I spent a week trying to find one. I contacted countless translators that week. I sent them sample pages with the most complex and poetic paragraphs and got the same answers from all of them: "It's challenging to translate these metaphors, poetic and long sentences into English. It won't make sense for British people." I found two translators who said they could translate the book, but they also mentioned a fee of about ten thousand pounds and a period of seven or eight months. I couldn't afford it; also, I didn't have time to wait seven months.

There was nothing I wouldn't do to have my baby published in English. So yet again, I had to contact someone from the Turkish community, a journalist this time. He liked the sample pages I sent him so much he wanted to read the whole book. I sent the manuscript to him. About a week later, he said, "Your writing ability is fantastic. However, no English man would experience love in this way. Your love, friendships, your descriptions about the places you visited, all that about your cringe-making ideas about England and British people. You are a sycophant."

He accused me of humiliating my own country and people. He hung up on me, saying, "There is no way I would ever help you with a book like this."

It took me a day to get over the impact of what that man had said.

After a rather depressing day, I made an insane

decision: I would translate it myself. But my level of English was not that good; how on earth was I going to do it when translators with years of experience were saying, "I can't translate this!!" But what choice did I have?

And on February 27, I started translating the book from Turkish to English. Of course, I couldn't do it entirely on my own with my English, and I had the help of Google Translate, Grammarly, and dictionaries. The days of sleep deprivation, hunger, thirst, endless cups of Turkish coffee and cigarettes had started again. Meanwhile, Bobby replied to my letter via WhatsApp and blocked me again. He was furious that I was using what had happened between us as material for a book. I couldn't reply to him. There was no point writing back, because I would give my answer with the book. So I had to translate the book into English at top speed.

As the days progressed and the number of pages I translated increased, I fell into a void. Not psychologically, but because I don't know if my translation would make any sense. After I started it, I came clean with my housemates in 3 Hilsea Street. I told them that I was actually writing a book about us, trying to translate it myself using Google Translate because I could not afford translator fees. Although we all made fun of this madness, including me, they patted me on the back and supported me. So, I translated a complicated paragraph in which I used the most intricate language and metaphors, shared it on the WhatsApp group and asked if they understood anything from what was written. They said the only sentence I hate in English, "It does not make sense".

I should have been depressed by this, given up, but I didn't. I grabbed hold of Stephen, pleading with him, and, on his advice, I worked on translating that most difficult paragraph into English again. Finally after two days, he sat down beside me, read what I had written, and looked at me with his smoky blue eyes and said, "Now, it makes sense. Wow! I wish someone would love me like this. I wish someone would write words like these for me."

That's when I realized what I had to do.

My English was not good, but my Turkish was beyond perfect. First, I edited the Turkish language of the book to make it more simple, without changing its meaning, shortening the sentences, and then started the translation again.

As the number of pages I translated increased, I started to worry again. Yes, maybe the sentences retained their meaning, but I knew I was making countless grammar and word order mistakes. Even if I translated the book, it was not possible for me to publish it in this state. I then looked for an English book editor, and soon found out that anyone willing to take on the editing of a book of this nature would cost £4,000 or more.

I couldn't afford that.

I felt tired, exhausted because of the endless difficulties I was encountering with the book.

While continuing to translate and looking for an editor, Jane came to my mind. I had met Jane about two years ago at a meeting of an environmental organization where I could find open-minded people who could accept me with my bad English at a time when I couldn't touch England in England. I had translated protest placards into Turkish for her sometimes. She also worked at the same school in north London where I had spent that month doing several jobs at once for the salary of one.

Life, fate, coincidence, luck must have all played a part in this.

On March 5, I emailed Jane and sent 25 pages that I had translated as an example. Although she said there were many grammatical and structural mistakes, she loved my story, from only those few pages, and she agreed to help me, saying she would definitely work on the book for me. And for that, she did a favour that no one else would have been prepared to and asked for only 800 pounds.

I can hardly describe how I worked with such speed and determination and joy once she had agreed to work with me, and by the morning of April 12, I had the last five pages left to check for the last time in the translation I finished a few days ago. Seeing that I had just five pages left to look over that morning, I texted Giulia that I would send the book to Jane, and be free that evening. So that evening at 9:07 p.m. I sent Jane the book and turned off my computer.

As soon as I turned my screen off, the pain I had felt

after Bobby blocked me attacked me like a monster waiting , hidden in the corner. I ran to the kitchen. I wanted to see my friends, hug them. I was going to force them to go anywhere, go out, have a few drinks to celebrate the end of the lockdown and the re-opening of the pubs. What a very nice coincidence that I finished the translation of my book too!

But I couldn't.

Because no one was home! They had all gone out together. Without calling me, without even bothering to ask if I would like to come. While I was checking the last lines of the translation, I heard Stephen, Manuel and Jeff calling to each other and getting ready to go out. "Wait for me too," Giulia was screaming to them. As they left the house laughing and leaving me at home, I put my friendship with them into 'an envelope' and threw it into the mailbox at Hilsea Street. When the time came, they would open 'the envelope'– my sequel – on the doormat and read it themselves.

While I was standing alone in the middle of the kitchen looking around, the monster sneaked down the stairs from my room, opened the kitchen door, jumped on me and grabbed me in its massive jaws. I didn't want to watch it devouring my flesh between its sharp teeth, and to relieve my pain, I scanned the room and saw an unfinished bottle of red wine on the counter. I had done my translation; I was all alone; I was stuck fast between the sharp teeth of a ravenous monster. Although it might not be the last wish of a dying person, there was nothing else to do, so I opened the wine bottle, put it in my mouth and drank it down in one long gulp.

Then I texted Giulia that I had come to the realization, once again, as a friend, I had no place among them.

She replied back that they had made the decision to go out on the spur of the moment, while sitting in the kitchen, and had just all spilled out of the house there and then. She apologized and wrote that they were waiting for me. But this was an hour later now.

So I didn't go.

After Giulia, Stephen texted me a few times, but I didn't reply to him. I spotted an unopened wine bottle on the counter, took it, went out into the garden, lit a cigarette. I put my earphones in and started listening to heavy rock music at full volume. I was beginning to feel the drunken effects of the half bottle of wine I had gulped. Under more normal circumstances, I would have stopped drinking at that point. But I had completed the months-long process of writing a book and then the translation that had drained my mind. I needed some relaxation. I didn't want to be drunk, but here I was, left alone on such an important day for me. Frankly, I couldn't find anyone else to celebrate with but myself. As I arguing with myself about drinking alcohol, suddenly Otto slammed the wine glass on the coffee table to the ground with his paw and smashed it so I wouldn't get too drunk.

"I'll drink from the bottle, then," I told him.

He jumped onto my lap to stop me, hugged my arms, jumped on my legs. While I was downing the wine, he did everything to distract and stop me. I struggled with Otto. I drunk the wine as fast as I could while the loud music blasted into my ears. When the Hilsea crowd came home and turned on the kitchen light, Otto jumped down and walked a distance away from me, but he didn't scamper off this time. He continued to look at me sadly, from where he was sitting on the grass in front of me.

Realizing I was in the garden, Giulia came out. She was saying something to me, but I couldn't hear her. I was refusing to take out my earphones. I glared at her angrily, kept drinking the wine, and then turned my head away from her again.

When she realized that I wasn't going to talk, she started texting me on WhatsApp. Admitting that she had made a mistake not letting me know they were going out even though she knew I would have finished my work in the evening, and then said she didn't see my text, apologizing to me profusely, reminding me she was my best friend, my little sunshine. I actually forgave her for acknowledging her mistake. I wanted to take out my earphones and hug her, but I just couldn't.

Because the Gods had whispered to me a few days ago.

Nor was I feeling very amiable because of the pain inflicted on me by that monster.

When I didn't respond to her attempts to say sorry, after several minutes, she became angry with me and turned on her heel and went back to the kitchen. Otto was standing there, still staring at me intently.

"What?" I asked him angrily, and I went to the kitchen.

Everyone in the house was sitting around the table sipping their drinks, listening to what happened from Giulia. I couldn't hear them, but I knew very well that they were talking about me. I stood by the garden side door and looked into their eyes, one by one, angrily. I didn't want to sit next to them.

On the way up to my room, I remembered my laundry that I had thrown into the washing machine earlier that day. Usually I would just gather it all up in my arms and take it to hang on the clothes rack in the bathroom. But in my fury and drunken state, I dropped some small items on the floor. I picked up the falling clothes and clasped them in my arms, but other bits escaped. I got angrier, and I left the laundry on the floor. I opened the kitchen cabinet next to the washing machine, pulled out the roll of black bin bags, and tried to tear off a bag to stuff the laundry inside. But as ever, I couldn't find the jagged edge to tear a bag off. So I threw the roll of bags on the floor and let the whole lot unravel. I tossed the damp laundry onto the length of unfurled bags, scooped it all up in one, and stood up.

At that moment, I saw that everyone was saying something to me, gesturing to me. I still couldn't hear what they were saying because of my earphones. I was furious with them, and drunk. Saying anything at that point would have unnecessary nasty consequences. I realized that. I just wanted to hang the laundry on the clothes rack, go to my room and sleep.

But I couldn't leave the kitchen.

Stephen was sitting in front of me, his chair blocking my way, saying something to me and getting no response. They were all yelling at me to listen to them, I could tell. I could see Stephen's face was flushed and the veins stood out on his neck. Stephen blocked my way no matter which side I went. "Not now," I said. I didn't want to get into a nasty argument. I was shouting at the top of my voice, not modulating my tone because of the music still blasting in my ears.

Realizing that Stephen wouldn't move out of my way, I tried to climb onto the counter and get past. Jeff pulled me from behind, and I fell into Stephen's lap. I jumped up to my feet again, squeezed through the tiny gap behind Stephen's chair, and started to walk off. At that moment, Manuel stopped me in panic and pointed towards Stephen. When I turned round, I saw the roll of garbage bags which I had gathered in my lap had wrapped themselves around his neck and were almost choking him.

Under normal circumstances, we would have all fallen into hysterical laughter at this. I wanted to laugh too, but I couldn't. Because another thing, only three days ago, with the exception of my little sunshine Giulia, no one had remembered my birthday. Not one of them had written the two-word 'Happy Birthday' greeting on the WhatsApp group until Giulia shared a photo we took together. Even Manuel,who came home late in the evening with flowers, had remembered that it was my birthday, thanks to his boyfriend Scott. But not the others, who I had shared so much time with. Feeling wholly excluded for the second time in just three days, and due to the pain of that monster's sharp teeth, no, I didn't laugh.

I freed Stephen's neck from the bags. I opened the door while trying to find the jagged edge of the bag. I stood in the doorway, fought with the roll of bin bags while my friends continued to stare at me in astonishment. When I failed, I pulled the roll along and started to climb the stairs towards my room, with the metres-long tail of black bin bags trailing behind me. Four steps before I reached my room, the end of the bags must have been stuck in the kitchen door as I couldn't go any further. Even though I tugged with all my might, the bags would not split. Finally, Jeff came up behind me and ripped the bag off and I could get into my room. I threw the laundry on my bed, then remembering I should hang it up, scooped it up and stuffed it all into the bin bag. Manuel was standing at my door just as I was about to leave the room. He kept talking at me, and I still couldn't hear him. "Not now, leave me alone!" I kept shouting, unable to adjust the volume of my voice.

Manuel accepted the fact there was no point in talking

to me and went back down to the kitchen. After he left, I locked my door, pushed the metres of bin bags onto the floor and lay down. I couldn't stand the smallness of that box room with those goddamn bags sweeping around me. In my drunken state, I started throwing everything around. As I tossed things into the air in the tiny room, I nearly knocked the potted orchid Giulia had given me on my birthday onto the ground. Knowing the effects of my craziness in that tiny room would have no limits, I left the flower in front of Giulia's bedroom door to avoid the pot being smashed. After I wrote dozens more lines, I felt that I had changed. I certainly didn't want to turn into the same Dilek again. Then I threw myself on the bed and fell asleep.

When I opened my eyes in the morning, the Gods had whispered to me, "You have to move, as soon as possible!"

I got up, tidied the mess in my room. When I checked my phone before I went to have a shower, I saw Giulia's text, "Wow! You even gave your birthday present back! I can not believe you! I can't believe you could destroy our bond so quickly. Yes, I made a mistake; I apologize. I apologized to you many times when I got home. But you didn't take out your earphones and listen to me. You didn't care what I texted you on WhatsApp. As you fought with the bin bags, I realized you were so drunk, so I didn't care what you were doing at that moment until I saw that flower outside the door to my room! Is our friendship that irrelevant for you? I can't believe you!"

Effects, reactions, misunderstandings.

It shouldn't have been like this. After turning to my writing, regaining my words and power, and transforming myself into another Dilek, this should not have happened. I texted Giulia explaining why I put the flower at her door and said I wanted to meet her after her work.

I was persuading myself that until the hour came to meet Giulia, I had to listen to what the whispers were saying to me. But I didn't know if I would find the strength to move from 3 Hilsea Street, to leave the people in that house, even though we had a few problems between us. I stared at the silence in the house as I went down to the kitchen and made myself something to eat. As usual, Agata had locked herself in her room to work. Manuel had gone to school, Stephen, Jeff and Giulia to work. I mean, the house was just as it always was. Although we were in lockdown, the others weren't at home that much. Agata worked in her room all day, Jeff and Stephen went out to work, and before she found a job, Giulia would stay with her boyfriend sometimes four days in a row.

I didn't feel that lonely until Matt moved out of the house because I used to sit all day in the kitchen with him. Although he had to spend much of the time talking to his customers on the phone, with the beautiful music he played on the loudspeaker, the conversations we had whenever he had a moment, it was good for me. I did the same with Manuel after Matt moved out, until the universities opened and he started school. And then Giulia found a job. So that all week I was by myself in the house. I would wait for the Friday nights to see them most of the time. But now lockdown was over, and everyone would return to their real life outside. Free at last. Those Fridays when we got together would no longer exist probably, and I would continue to spend every day on my own. When I couldn't stand my loneliness any more, I would do something unnecessary to attract their attention.

I didn't want to do that.

I had spent months trying to transform myself into a new Dilek, to arrive on that island and give birth to my colourful children. And I didn't want it to be all broken by my fear of loneliness. I promised myself that I would find the strength to listen to those whispers, as I sat eating alone in the kitchen.

In the evening, I picked up Giulia in front of her workplace. When we saw each other, we hugged tightly, like two old friends who haven't seen each other for many years. Then we started looking for a place to sit and have a drink. When it came to Giulia and me, even this most ordinary of activities could turn into a comedy. Our adventure, which started on Harley Street, ended at Tapas Bravas at the foot of Tower Bridge. Over exactly five hours, we finished two bottles of rosé and poured out whatever had been hurting us; we apologized to each other. The more we did this, the more we laughed and hugged. And we proved that our friendship was solid.

When we entered the house that evening, we saw the other house members in the kitchen as a happy chance. At first the others were a little surprised to see Giulia and me tied together more tightly than ever. Then they apologized to me – even though they had sometimes not hesitated to push my door open while I was writing my book and doing translation – because they didn't think of letting me know me that day when they were going out. Everyone apologized, forgave and hugged each other.

Following our reconciliation, everyone went to their rooms because they had to get up early the next day. But Giulia was off; she wasn't going to work. We had another two bottles of rosé wine, and we went to my Pandora Box room together. When we finished them, it was half-past eleven in the morning. We leant against each other on my bed, unable to move our fingers, chatting about religions. Giulia said that she had to be at her friend's birthday party at three o'clock. She urged me to come with her because she couldn't stand going on her own. I told her if we went to Stevenage, to Bobby's after the birthday party, I would go with her.

"Okay,", she said, "We could go, but have a look in the mirror; we both look miserable. Bobby has seen you in your pyjamas every time. Do you want him to see you again in your pyjamas and in this drunken state? I don't want to meet him like this either," making me less keen on plan. But, indecisive, we revisited the argument, every five minutes, between religion, cultures and other serious topics, while we sat shoulder to shoulder as we tried to make up our minds what to do. And we fell asleep as we talked and tried to decide.

Everything was back to normal at Hilsea Street, and everyone went back to their lives. That is to say, back to the outside world. While translating my book, Stephen had told me that he had rented his friend's flat who had returned to Italy, so I could take over his room. I even found another person to move into my box room after Stephen moved to his new house and I took his room. But I was not going to move into the room. The time had come for me to take the next step. Even though I knew the answer, I had to ask that question and get the answer in real life. I mean, I had to prove whether my bond with the members of 3 Hilsea Street was reality or the illusion of people who had had to stay together due to lockdown and managed that period wonderfully. And, of course, I had to find a place where I wasn't trying to get anyone's attention, where I didn't behave in an unnecessary way, where I could face what real loneliness means and overcome that fear. To raise my children waiting to grow up like Daniel, his seven warriors, and Wilbert; to give birth to many more waiting to be born.

At that point, I didn't have the strength to look for a new room, and I decided to go to Turkey. I wanted to hug my mother a million times, the longing for her had become unbearable; to see my brothers and spend time with my spiritual sister Gulbahar, and my real friends there. My divorce case was to be heard on April 29. Then after a month, I would be able to get rid of X's cursed surname and return to my own.

That's why I decided to go to Turkey at the end of May, when the time would have come when I could start the process of changing my surname. When I told the Hilsea Street housemates that I would be going to Turkey and staying there for a long time, Agata said, "I also want to go to Poland, to see my family. You are a very lucky person. I'm so jealous of you."

While looking at her, I was also testing the new Dilek I had created inside me. Even though we know they won't change, can we continue to be nice to people, try to purge them of unnecessary jealousy? I had been looking for answers with her to those questions since I moved into the house.

"Actually, I am going to Turkey for my cancer treatment. I didn't tell you, but I was diagnosed early on my last trip to Turkey. I came back to England to finish the book. I've finished my work, and it's time to start the treatment," I said, looking into Agata's eyes.

The next day, while I was making my coffee in the kitchen, Agata came and hugged me. "I'm so jealous of you for going to Turkey and seeing your family. I want to go back to my family and never come back here," she said again.

"You know that I am going to Turkey for my cancer treatment."
"Well, you will still see your family, won't you? You are lucky. I wish I were you."
"You can be, Agata. No one is forcing you to stay

here. You are both a European and a UK citizen. You don't have a visa problem. You can live wherever you want. You don't have family here; you don't have a man you love; you don't have friends – as you say. You don't even like the people in this house or join in with us most evenings. All the time, you say you're sick of this country, you don't like the British. You say that your life in Poland is much better. You say your homeland is Poland and you only feel you belong there. So why are you here, Agata? Why do you live in a country that you don't like and feel you don't belong? To make a little more money?"

I nodded, smiling at her with disgust and contempt, "You're the one who chose to live in a country where you don't belong and become an immigrant just for money, so do not whinge in front of me again," I said.

I went to the garden, sat on the bench Stephen had made one foot short and started drinking my coffee. Daniel came and sat next to me. As we were sitting in silence, Otto jumped onto the table. He noticed Daniel and started sniffing the God lurking in those specks of dust that only the two of us could see. "I wish…" I said as I was looking at Otto and smiled at his bewildered gaze, trying to figure out who this man he had seen for the first time was. But Daniel stopped me.

"You can't wish! You are a million light-years away from even asking such a thing," he said with an affectionate smile.
"Why some people…?" Then he stopped me again.
"Don't keep stopping me. I just want to talk to you a

little bit."

"When you enter my world, you will understand why. That's why I can't let you talk now."

"Well. At least, I wish you could drink Turkish coffee too. Fortune tells me, you are a God, you can see my future!" I said to him, smiling mischievously.

"Why do you want to see more than you can see even though you know you can't change it? Don't give yourself more pain!"

I nodded my head approvingly. The three of us sat there in silence. "Tell Stephen to fix this and make a backrest we can lean on," Daniel said, tired of my rocking the bench.

"You are God; whisper it to him too," I replied with a laugh.

Even though I was going to move out, I didn't want to spend my time just waiting for Jane to finish the editing and the day came to go to Turkey. I needed to earn more money so I could extend my time in London. I had thought of a way where I could make a lot of money very quickly. I contacted one of my friends in Turkey; I told her what I had in mind, and she said she would be able to help me. When I learned this, I presented the offer to my existing customer; she liked it and accepted it. I earned five thousand pounds in twenty minutes with two ten-minute phone calls and two e-mails for the job. Thus, I guaranteed that I could stay in England for one more year with the money I had saved.

For months I had locked myself in my room and

worked for days without sleeping, so I had deserved some rest. I fed my soul with that calm green of London parks. I walked around the streets, watched people, longed for London by walking thousands of steps in a week. Then I wanted to do something at home. Unfortunately, because of Stephen, the garden was in a state of chaos as usual. For three days, I cleaned and tidied the garden up. Just a few hours later, Stephen came and left his materials in the garden as usual for the art workshop he was doing for his students, and the garden fell into disarray again.

Watching him with weary resignation, I asked him if he needed the wood lying on the ground. When he said didn't, I said, "I will make a bench for the garden with it then."

I took the drill from his hand and asked him, "How do you use it? Teach me, please."

For a few minutes, he made fun of my wanting to make a bench without even knowing how to use a drill. However, as I cut and shaped the wood and fought with the drill, as those minutes progressed and the bench slowly started to form, Stephen watched me with huge surprise and a bit enviously. Three hours later, my battle with the wood and the drill was over. Except for a few blocks of wood that Stephen helped me cut, I had made a bench by myself in three hours. A bench as beautiful and sturdy as the ones in the parks. Everyone came out into the garden in surprise and admiration, and they kept asking how I had done it.

After everyone went back to their rooms, I made my nightly coffee and sat on the bench. Daniel and Otto came, and the three of us sat side by side on the bench.

"Yes, now I can sit more comfortably and with pleasure. You did a good job," Daniel said with a smile.
"Thank God for the wood," I said, laughing at him.

Two days later, Stephen had finished his work, arranged the garden and flowers in his own way, and went on holiday with his family. After he left, I changed the garden the way I wanted it. We had repeated this never-ending cycle for a year. The arrangement was not enough for me this time, because I was bored with that dark blue colour on the garden walls. I bought cream-coloured paint, painted the garden walls, planted new flowers, bought lights, and decorated the whole garden with them.

The kitchen pots were in bad nick. I bought two top quality pans, six elegant and expensive plates, some kitchen items and flowers to put in the kitchen. As all this was clearly costing money, Agata began to panic, saying that she was financially tight and didn't want to spend unnecessary money on the house.

"Did anyone ask you for money? I didn't ask you while making or buying any of this; I don't want the others' money either," I said.

She was shocked. "You are crazy," she said, smiling with her usual demeanour.

"I don't want your money, but I did expect you to say thank you instead of being rather rude, Agata. Everyone has their limits, believe me. I don't have to accept that kind of thanks," I retaliated.

"Okay," she said, hugging me tightly, "Thank you, crazy woman. I'm sorry, you know I… Anyway, but please tell me how much you spent and we'll split it between us. I'm sure you spent a lot," she said.

"Maybe I just want to spend money and do something nice for this house," I said to her.

I was in a state of euphoria all day. There were only a few hours to go before I achieved what I had been fighting for for six years, so I had wanted to share my happiness by doing something good. Because the next day, April 30, at 10 am, my divorce case was being heard, and I could finally be a free woman after all my struggles. When I returned to my room, feeling warm and excited, my cousin, who is my lawyer, called me towards midnight.

He was laughing like crazy, "A national lockdown had been declared again just a few minutes ago. Nothing will open tomorrow."
"They announced it in the middle of the night on a Thursday?"
"Well, you know your own country, its rulers..."
"What will happen now?"
"They will give us a new date. The lockdown will last for a month, probably by the end of May."
"Fuck."

I had told Jane I wanted to publish the book at the beginning of June and asked her to finish editing accordingly by that date. With this unexpected change of dates, I sent her an email explaining that the case was postponed, that there was no need to hurry, that she had time for editing until the end of June. She had earlier sent me an email saying that the book was very long, that she understood what I was trying to say, but that I made rather a lot of grammatical errors and that it was challenging to work through it in the time I gave her. When she saw the email I sent, "I didn't think I would be glad that you didn't get your divorce," she replied. I laughed!

The next evening, when I explained the situation, my housemates were surprised and saddened. Then I told them I would probably not come back to England again; therefore, I was going to rent out my new room (Stephen's old one). Agata wasn't happy with her room, so I suggested she move into that room before putting up an ad.

"Of course, you're only asking me because you would like to get your deposit back quickly," she said.
"I'm asking you because I know you've always wanted to move into that room. I can easily get my deposit back because I can get a tenant for that room in a day."
"No, you can't. Put an ad up and see."

Stephen was moving out of his room at the end of May, and I had to find a tenant by then. But I couldn't advertise the room because Stephen was on holiday with his family and had locked his door. Until my moving day came, I sorted out the belongings that I would give to the charity shop again. A few months ago, I had given everything to a charity shop, and I had kept only my laptop in the room, the clothes I was wearing, and my drawing pad. Within a month or two, I had suitcases full of stuff again! I couldn't understand how this could happen in that tiny room.

My divorce date was now set for May 29. I didn't want to wait until the beginning of July to go to Turkey to change my last name. I bought my ticket for May 22 because the PCR test requirement to enter Turkey would be lifted that day. I only had a one-way ticket. I was leaving No. 3 Hilsea Street, I was going to relinquish my room, and when I got back, I had no idea what would happen or where I would stay. But all my instincts, and those whispers, were telling me to seek out my solitude.

When Stephen told me he would be back on 17 May, I repeated the offer I made to Agata, and she gave me the same answer. When she found out that I was leaving England a week later, she got worried and said, "You can't find a person who we like and say 'yes' to in that short time."

"It will take me a day to find someone." I told her.

I wrote the perfect ad, and put it on Facebook on the Hackney Wick Space, the traditional room search page for east Londoners. In just an hour, dozens of people had shown interest in the room. While I was replying to them, a room advertisement caught my eye on the page. It was an ad for a room for £475 a month, a lot more than my budget. However, those whispers were starting to speak to me again. I sent a message to the person who'd posted the ad and made an appointment to see the house and the room the next day.

When I went to see the house, I met Lia. She came to the door of that arty building I was standing in front of and let me in. I experienced something very strange when I met her for the first time. I could see her but couldn't hear what she was talking about. I couldn't even understand what Daniel was talking about. Lia on one side and Daniel on the other were gesturing to me, but I was deaf. Because of those whispering cries from this historic building and the hurricane-like energy coming my way from Lia. She grabbed me by the hand, lifted me from my seat at top speed and dragged me into a hurricane with her! And all I could hear in the tempest were the whispered screams of the Bow Quarter.

There was something about this woman. I didn't know what. What was waiting for me?

I didn't like the room, but I liked Lia and the Bow Quarter whisperers' from the very first moment. She seemed to like me too, and she texted me half an hour after I left. I hadn't seen the other house members, nor had they seen me. I had even forgotten to see the bathroom, and Lia had forgotten to show me it too. While I was leaving the house, Lia told me it would take about a week for them to see the other fifteen candidates, and if they decided on me, I had to meet the other house members before I moved in. But I had already paid my deposit to my new landlord. I had made the deal to meet my real loneliness, just half an hour after leaving Bow Quarter. Since the room was empty, I could move in whenever I wanted.

Is it stupid to believe in energies -in a good or bad way-, when humans, animals, everything that exists in the world is made up of atoms, molecules, electrons, microscopic organisms that cannot be seen with the naked eye?

On the way home, I wrote to the house WhatsApp group that I wanted us to get together for the last time as No. 3 Hilsea Street before returning to Turkey. We agreed to have a farewell party on Friday, May 21. I was back home and making myself some food in the kitchen. Then Agata came to the kitchen, "Stephen's room is bigger, prettier, and cheaper than mine. I've been living here for seven years, and the new tenant will pay less than me. This is not acceptable. Withdraw the ad and change the rent," she was yelling at me like crazy.

If she had just cried or made her case calmly, I would have done as she told me. But I was so angry that she was yelling at me in her usual aggressive way. I had my limits, and they had been reached some time ago now. I started yelling back at her, and for the first and last time at 3 Hilsea Street, I had a full-blown argument with someone there. When she understood I was done with her, she went to her room, still crying.

I sent a long message to the WhatsApp group

repeating what I said to her: "Agata, I told you many times to move into Stephen's room; you didn't want it. You knew what the rent was for the room, and you didn't say anything about it. I have arranged viewing appointments with seventeen people on this rent. If you have a problem with your rent, you should talk to the landlord. Come to your senses, get a grip; enough is enough."

After Agata's outburst, I had dropped the second bomb in the middle of Hilsea Street. After I had sent that message, everyone in the WhatsApp group started to bicker and got upset. The house had been shaken by such a massive earthquake for the first time, and a deep silence had fallen upon everyone.

Seventeen people came to see the room between 9 in the morning to 8 in the evening on May 17. Jeff, Manuel and Agata were surprised how I had managed to sift through the hundreds of candidates and arrange the viewing on the same day. Because some people came a little late, some a little early, some of them liked the house so much, and we couldn't send them away, at one point during the day the house was full with three of the tenant candidates and their friends.

At eight o'clock in the evening, after seeing the last candidate, we sat at the kitchen table, our heads aching from talking to people all day. Jeff, Agata and Manuel thanked me for finding so many good candidates, and debated who they would choose.

Meanwhile, Giulia had come home from work. She sent me a message on WhatsApp saying that she and

Agata were going to have a drink and called me to join them. I had chatted with Agata throughout the day as if there were no problems between us in front of the candidates. However, I had no intention of forgiving her before she apologized to me and admitted her mistake.

Although Giulia was not at home on the day of the discussion, she had responded to Jeff's ultimatum on the chat: "Agata, we don't want you in this house."

"This is too much Jeff," Guilia posted.

I know Giulia was offering to fix our problems, but I couldn't agree to her request because she hadn't even asked me what had actually happened. So, I started to argue with Giulia too via texts.

In that evening they decided on their new housemate and the tenant paid the deposit to me. I packed my two suitcases that evening, left 3 Hilsea Street and slept in my new home. The next day I moved my stuff in Jeff's van. When Jeff found out I was moving to another house, he thought I was lying to them. He was offended, but he understood when I explained what had happened. He was speechless when he saw the Bow Quarter and my new home, and he was pleased for me that I had found such a nice place to live. I told him that I was very angry with the girls, and that it was not a good idea to get together at that time and so cancelled my farewell party. Still, Jeff, Stephen and Manuel wanted to say goodbye properly before I went to Turkey. So we met at Hackney Wick on the night of Friday, May 21, and had a couple of beers and said goodbye.

That evening, Giulia wrote to me how sorry she was about what had happened and that she didn't want to lose me. I told her that she hadn't lost me, that nothing had changed in our friendship, that I only wanted to see her after my nerves had settled. We were reconciled again. But when the guys returned home and she learned they had been with me, Giulia was very angry that we had met up without her. She wrote me a farewell message that ended our friendship, saying that what I had done was unacceptable, but she ended: "But no matter what, I love you very much, and you will always be in my heart."

I replied to her, "I didn't do it out of revenge, but I think you can understand now how I felt when you went out without me the day lockdown was over. Neither you nor I need to end this friendship. We only need to get away from each other for a bit and calm down. Believe me, after a while, you will agree with me. I love you very much, and you too are always in my heart."

And so, I started the process that would answer the question whether my friendships at 3 Hilsea Street were real or just an illusion of lockdown. I would be introduced to true loneliness, but overcome my fear of being alone and add a new dimension to my writing.

I stayed four nights in my new home. My instincts had been right. After Lia, I also met Jake and Josh the day I moved in. I liked them. But the house, like No. 3 Hilsea Street, had six tenants, and there was also a group of six 'next-door neighbours' who were always in the house. Even though I couldn't meet with the others, I felt it in my bones that this house would be where I would go through the difficult process that would completely transform me into the Dilek I wanted to be and to cope with being alone. So I went to Turkey knowing that I had to prepare for this process.

I asked my spiritual sister Gulbahar to be witness at my divorce case. She had been offended when I didn't make her witness at my wedding with X. While I was laughing through my screams and tears of happiness after the court case, I told her: "You see; you have witnessed something much better than my marriage." My seven-year struggle was over; no one in my family was harmed; I was still alive, and had not become a murderer by killing X. I had survived. Gulbahar and I lay on the grass in Kadikoy, looked up at the trees, the uniquely beautiful view of Istanbul, the blue sea, and the ferries gliding over it. We filled our souls with the sheer joy of living, with the evening sun shining on us while we laughed and made fun of everything, especially ourselves. I looked at Gulbahar while we lay there. I had no idea what I would do if I didn't talk to her almost every day for hours. She was my rock, to stand that fucking marriage and the abuse X had inflicted on me. She was my heart, my smile. She was my everything, even though we had to live far apart.

During the forty-two days I stayed in Turkey, as ever

I kept up with the crazy energy of my eight-year-old niece, Elif, and became a child again with her. I returned to my mischievous youth with my spiritual sister Gulbahar and my other real friends. I held my mother close, smelled her, breathed in her scent, and was reborn with every breath. I thanked God a million times that I had such a mother, that she trusted me so much. She was a strong woman who loved to tell stories; she had them in her genes and soul, and she had bequeathed her talents to me. I am so thankful to her because she dedicated herself only to her children. Instead of watching TV all day like other mothers, she taught me to read and write when I was five years old, told the stories and asked, "What is the meaning of this story?" I am so thankful to her because when I started primary school at the age of five, and didn't like the school and refused to do my homework, she took my tiny hands in her palm and made a deal with me as she said: "Perseverance can break all unbreakable walls." In other words, she taught me to never give up, however hard the challenge.

It was my mother who made me into an indestructible woman.

I hugged my brothers dozens of times too. I thanked God I have them because although we always argue and fight when we are together, we can love, forgive, and support each other.

And I saw my father. It was some years since I had seen him last. We didn't hug. We never did. He couldn't show his love to me, like he couldn't show it to any of us. He continued to speak only the truth of what he believed, as always. I watched my father for days, whom I always saw as a physical strength, but who couldn't give us the love of a father. Even though my big-hearted mother gave us the love of both mother and father, should I thank my father too for being the first and foremost person to create the breach and wounds in my heart that will never heal? Still, I thanked God for having such a father. He was a recluse and had passed on those genes to me that would give me the strength to deal with my own loneliness.

I felt refreshed and prepared for the final battle to complete the new me. I returned to England on Tuesday, 29 June 2021. We were loaded onto buses from Heathrow Airport and brought to the Sofitel Hotel in the environs of Gatwick Airport.

From the moment we got off the bus, we were thrown thousands of kilometres away from the kindness of the passport control officer I encountered on my very first arrival in England. Our PCR tests were negative, and we were not sick. However, they treated us as if we had the most virulent illness, or like dangerous prisoners, from the moment they passed us in turn through the hotel doors. When it was my turn to register, I went across to the staff sitting at the table set in the middle of the lobby. While the man held my documents and brusquely took down all my details onto a form in front of him, he asked me for a name and phone number they could reach in an emergency.

"I have no one," I said.
"How so?"
"I have no one in England. I am entirely alone."

"There must be someone."

I wanted to say, "I have some friends, I have Giulia, and the metal of that relationship has been tested," but I didn't. And I gave him Josh's number instead. While I was giving the number to the officer, my loneliness emanated from me to crush him. It was my loneliness filling out the questions on that form at that table. It was a legal procedure, before they gave me my visa to the land of solitude.

"Do you think that your loneliness is your fault?", "Do you think that you are lonely because you give too much love to people?", "Do you think that people you have not met, talked to on the phone or messaged for a long time are your friends?", "Do you think because the people you want to meet are busy all the time, it means that you have no value in their eyes?", "Do you think real friendship needs to pass some test?", "Do you think no matter what you've done, people don't like you?"

I continued to ask myself these questions as I walked towards my room accompanied by two security guards. I looked around at my surroundings, and at the security guards placed every five metres along the corridors. As soon as we entered the hotel, I realised that the quarantine conditions and the atmosphere here would be much worse than I had imagined. I understood all too well now what a death row prisoner feels while walking along those corridors. Still, I relaxed a bit when I saw my room and its large window.

Two days passed until Josh sent me my laptop. Over this time, the worsening pain of leaving my family and friends, and the necessity of being enclosed in a room where it was forbidden to even open the door, turned into a nightmare. I had watched all the programmes on TV, but the hours wouldn't budge. My room was large and beautiful, the double bed was very comfortable, and the view was beautiful from my window. But the behaviour of the staff, the food left in paper bags at the door of my room, were disgusting.

While we were imprisoned in the rooms, tens of thousands of people had gathered to sing in the streets and pubs for the European Cup, regardless of the virus. If the food had been good, if my window would have opened, if I could have breathed fresh air, if I could have drunk my Turkish coffee with my cigarette, and if I hadn't been watching the joy of those fans on the screens, I admit it, that I wouldn't have cared about beyond the door of my room and the quarantine wouldn't have been that much of a drama. By the afternoon of the second day, I was thoroughly overwhelmed by the hum of the air conditioner. I was afraid that I wouldn't be able to stay in that prison with that hum for ten days, and I would go crazy. We were only allowed out once a day, to walk around the hotel carpark for just fifteen minutes.

I felt so awful, I called security, and they sent two security guards an hour later.

Once again, luck smiled on me. Two grinning, talkative, humorous English security guards came to pick me up. When I told Jimmy and Owen, who were in their mid-twenties, that it was my second day and I was feeling horrible, they kept me out for an extra fifteen minutes. As we paced together in the garden outside the hotel, chatting and laughing, a man with a broken accent approached angrily, pulled them aside and scolded them. Jimmy and Owen quickly took me to my room.

"What did that man say to you? I understood that he was angry with you. I hope I didn't cause you any trouble?" I asked them.

They laughed, saying, "Don't worry about it," and they taught me a fantastic trick. Those excellent two lads told me if I call the security after seven o'clock and tell them I didn't go out in the morning, since they are so busy and can't check the room numbers, I could go out again. Thanks a million times to Jimmy and Owen, I was able to get out twice a day.

When I got my laptop in the evening of the second day, and I had the idea of brewing the coffee I had brought from Turkey in a kettle, all my problems were solved. I put in my earphones, got rid of the voice of the howling air conditioner, sat at my desk in front of my large window overlooking the airport on one side and that little forest on the other, and started checking out the edit Jane had sent me. I started working without sleep again.

I didn't care about the disgusting food, my hunger, or the lack of oxygen in the room. Apart from Jimmy and Owen, and their colleagues Mike and Georgi, who always accompanied me with their friendly conversations, I didn't care about the dozens of other sullen and rude security guards I also came across. I wasn't really aware of where I was, what I was doing, or how many days I had left.

Whatever my circumstances were at that moment, I would continue smiling as I looked at the colours and the world in my book. I had succeeded. I was able to push everything aside and hold onto my words, and cure myself with them. I had produced a 442-page book with the new Dilek. Moreover, I had dared to do what a native level of English, who has lived in England for years and knows the culture and British perspective much better than me, didn't dare to do. Ignoring the moans of my lungs that could be heard two metres away, the blood coming out of my nose from the stress, the pain in my eyes; using dictionaries, Google Translate and Grammarly, I had finished the translation in a month and a half. And Jane had understood all my translation, didn't say, "makes no sense". Without needing to change a single point in my story, descriptions and metaphors, she had just corrected my sentences' grammatical and structural mistakes. Then she sent it back to me with a long complimentary email for my book.

Although I didn't notice how the days went by because I was working, when they called me from security around ten o'clock in the evening of 9 July and told me that I could leave the hotel after midnight, I replied, "I don't want to stay in this goddamn hotel for a second longer".

When I opened the door to my new home, Josh greeted me with a hug, helping me carry my luggage to my room. He said that the famous 'nextdoor neighbours', who were constantly talked about, were also in the living room. I had been trapped in a room for ten days and wanted to get out. I'd been locked in, unable to open my mouth and speak to anyone except when I didn't run into my security guard friends. Although I had prepared myself for the solitude that awaited me over those ten days, at that moment, I was in a dilemma. I hesitated between not being alone and getting some air.

"Hey, you know why you moved into this house," I reminded myself as I decided to go out but went down to the living room. Because Lia had left an envelope for me there.

After a short introduction to the people in the living room, I opened the large cardboard envelope that lay next to the TV. Tears came to my eyes and I smiled at the same time, looking at the thing in my hands. The others were curious, and I gave them a brief summary of the situation, what was the between my palms. They were surprised. Josh told them, "Dilek paints beautifully. I saw the sculpture you made as well; it's lovely."

As he talked, Agata's conversation with Stephen's girlfriend, which I had accidentally overheard, echoed on the faces of the people in the living room: "She manages to overcome all her problems, earns lots of money with two emails, writes books, translates, draws pictures, sculpts, designs beautiful jewellery, cleans the house without any bother, decorates the garden, paints the walls, buys things for the house with her own money. Now this bench is out there too! She built a bench in three hours without knowing how to use a drill. This girl is too much!"

Those ten minutes were enough. I was genuinely sure. This house would be the place of my solitude. I thought I had allowed my feelings to mislead me because of Lia, Jake and Josh being in the house. But Lia and Jake had moved to another house while I was in Turkey. During those ten minutes of sitting in the living room, I realized that I would even lose Josh because of those infamous 'nextdoor neighbours'. Once again, I accepted that I had to trust my instincts.

Then I went out, walked for minutes in the silent and dark garden of the Bow Quarter, accompanied by the whispers of a hundred years of history. After walking for about half an hour, I returned home. My room was no longer on the ground floor because Jake had moved to another house, and I moved to Jake's room. Now I would live on the third floor, again at the top of the tower, in a slightly larger room, next door to Josh. When I entered my new room, I couldn't believe my eyes when I saw how beautifully and carefully Josh had arranged my things. He had even organized my drawers. He came upstairs to get something from his room while I was looking around the room. When I saw him, I wanted to hug him to say thank you, but he was not a British guy like those in No. 3 Hilsea Street. I knew that it would take time for him to get used to these hugs, that we had yet to get through the tests ahead. That's why I could only thank him. "While you were in Turkey, you let me use your room and let my friends stay. I just wanted to thank you," he said to me.

After Josh returned to the living room, I sat on my bare bed, turned on my computer, and started doing the last thing I had to do to hold my baby between my palms in real life. I opened an account for myself on Amazon UK. It was half-past two in the morning when I started the account opening process. As I started working at full speed, my seven-year veteran laptop slowed down. "Don't die today, please," I pleaded with it. Fortunately, it was just a temporary death due to updates. About two hours later, at around half past four in the morning, I was able to use my computer again.

I did not expect the Amazon transactions to be so complex. It was around eight o'clock in the morning by the time I had opened an account. It was time to upload and publish my book. First, I had to prepare the book cover. Yes, the book's cover would be the painting Bobby had made as a sweet twist of fate for this book, but without Bobby's permission, however.

Bobby was still very angry with me for putting what happened between us in the book, and he had still blocked me from everywhere. I couldn't use that painting at the size it was on the Instagram post. And I knew that he wouldn't send it to me if I tried to buy a print of his painting via his Etsy account.

While Jane was editing the English edition of my book I had tried to buy the painting before I moved out of Hilsea Street and went to Turkey. Since Bobby knew my address, I couldn't ask my housemates to get it for me. And Matt was not in England at the time. So I asked for help from Eva, who was our neighbour in Hilsea Street's she lived at a different address. She warned me that I would be violating copyright, that it was illegal, and that Bobby could sue me for a tremendous amount if I used the painting.

"I know, but he won't do anything, you can be sure of that. You won't be in trouble, don't be afraid."

"This is a mistake. It's also wrong to use his real name in that book, despite the fact he told you he didn't want you to."

"I know him very well Eva, he won't do anything bad. Even though he is angry right now and doesn't understand me, in time, that anger will pass, and he will understand why I wrote this book. Just order the painting. Nothing will happen. Nevertheless, if something does, you can say that you weren't aware of the situation, and you'll get away with it. There's no way you'll get in trouble."

"You try first," she said. "If he sends it to you, it means he has given permission, and there will be no problem."

"Okay, I will order it, but he won't send it to me."

"Try anyway. If he doesn't, I'll think about whether to order it or not, I promise."

I was pissed off; to simply order a print shouldn't be this much of a problem. "You will think about it!" I said and went home, leaving Eva at that table forever. The day Eva refused to help me, I had no choice but to order the painting myself, and Bobby did what I expected and refused my order.

While making my final checks in the hotel room during my quarantine, I was brooding over how to take a high-resolution photo of that painting. As they were all living at different addresses now I could have asked Matt, Stephen, Manuel and certainly Josh to help me. But the whispers insisted that I ask Lia to buy that painting for me. Two days before I left the hotel, I sent a message to her explaining the situation, emphasizing that what she was going to do was illegal.

"Are you crazy? I wouldn't hesitate for a second if I could help you get your book published like you have been dreaming of. I don't know Bobby, I have no idea, but I don't feel like he's going to do anything," said Lia. She ordered the painting within thirty seconds.

About an hour later, she sent me a photo that shocked her and me both and gave us goosebumps.

It was a photo of Bobby and one of his best friends. I had never met him, but I knew from Bobby's Instagram posts that he was one of his closest friends. This was that person. He was someone that I mentioned in the Turkish version of the first book, but I had skipped a paragraph about him in the translation

– because I didn't want to mention his name. I had written about him after I mentioned Bobby's flatmate and my bad feelings about that flatmate. I wrote in the Turkish version of my book, *"I wish James were Bobby's flatmate. I never met him, but I always felt relaxed and at peace when I looked at his pictures with Bobby. If James were Bobby's flatmate, everything would be different. I can feel it. I wish I could meet him."* And I had told Giulia and Gulbahar at length all about my positive feelings about this friend of Bobby's.

But I couldn't translate that paragraph. I had already described nearly everything about Bobby, and I didn't want to put in another name about his life.
And now, a few months later, Lia had sent me that very same photo that I had shown to Giulia and Gulbahar, and where we talked for hours about James.

I read the message Lia had sent with the photo: "When I was ordering the painting, it was strangely familiar to me from somewhere. After placing the order, I wondered who Bobby was; I checked his Instagram account and was shocked. That man standing next to Bobby is my ex, and we still have a weird relationship that we haven't finished."

Life, destiny, coincidences!

While I was thinking of leaving 3 Hilsea Street without renting another room and going to Turkey, I had only looked at Lia's house because of those whispers. She had cancelled appointments with all the other candidates after I left the house, although she wasn't able to understand why she did this. And now we had a common bond that we never expected, that we wouldn't even have imagined in our wildest dreams. We were becoming close friends, and the men we had each fallen in love with were themselves two best friends!

I prepared the cover of the book, smiling to myself about this strange bond with Lia. Bobby had unknowingly drawn every detail of this painting so that it could be the cover. I cried. I wanted to hug Bobby and share the joy of this supernatural coincidence, destiny, whatever it is called, that the painting fit so perfectly on the cover of my book. It was 11:47 p.m. by the time I managed to prepare the cover and upload the book file to Amazon, despite my half-broken computer that was now bombing on and off. And I published my first English book on July 10, 2021, exactly three years after the day I stepped into England for the very first time, after a supernatural adventure.

I ran round to Lia, who was excitedly waiting for me in her new home two buildings away, after finishing my work. I hugged her, as she opened the door and cried, "I did it".

Then we started to talk about the amazing coincidence, about Bobby and James. While talking about James, I watched her movements, her gestures. I understood. I didn't want to understand, but unfortunately I got it. Sometimes, I hate it that I can understand even the smallest gesture people make, what they are actually thinking deep down and how they will act in the future. Sometimes... even though I know what they will do, I choose not to accept what I see in their souls and stay with them. But always... they do what I can see, deep in their souls. Although I could see everything about her through her gestures, I chose not to understand even though I knew what she would do to me. I decided to wait to see what colour she would choose. What colour would Lia add to my story? Would she choose to be white, help me, introduce me to James one day, and help me to reach out to Bobby again? Or would she choose to be black and instead of helping me, do something terrible to keep me from reaching James and Bobby? I left her house with these questions… that I already knew the answers to.

On 11 July there was the Euro finals match between England and Italy. That evening, I found myself watching the people sitting in the next-door neighbours living room rather than the game. Before they knew it, I had gone deep into their hearts and met parts of their selves they didn't even know about. And I understood what I had to do. I made my decision.

I was due to receive the first edition of my book on July 13. The fact that I'd forgotten to change my address meant my books were going to arrive at the house in 3 Hilsea Street. Manuel and Stephen no longer lived there. I thought about calling Giulia, but those whispers stopped me. They told me it wasn't the right time. I told Jeff that I would come round to Hilsea Street to pick up my order. When Jeff learned that I was back, he was delighted and said he was looking forward to seeing me.

When I went round to Hilsea Street on the evening of 13 July, Jeff opened the door. He hugged me tightly, telling me how much he had missed me, so many times, but he couldn't hide the very embarrassed expression on his face.

"Can we meet outside another time? Let's arrange a day when we're both available. Also, Manuel and Stephen can't wait to see you. We can all have fun together. Outside," he said in a shaky voice. He blushed.

"Give me my envelope," I said.

He handed me the cardboard envelope. "I'm so sorry, Dilek. Please don't be mad at me, please. Please! Dilek!" He was shouting at me. He was flustered, because he couldn't open that door to me because of Agata.

I had already turned the corner of the street as he continued to shout after me in agitation. Was I was supposed to be angry, offended? But I didn't feel anything. I didn't even care what had just happened. There were only feelings of happiness and pride in me as I touched my book in my palm. After walking for a while, I stopped, opened the envelope and looked at my book, my baby, my adventure, which started with a tiger in my dream in 2014 and finished seven years later, in 2021, with a stolen picture on the cover. Touching that book, the cover, the painting on the cover. I had made a work that could be turned into a movie, even only with that book cover story.

I did.

With Bobby.

We were two planets thrown towards each other from thousands of kilometres away, crashed at full speed, shattered, scattered, turned into a dust cloud, and created a new world from that dust cloud. Bobby remained silent; I made stories from his silence. He had unknowingly done the cover artwork for this book; I had managed to write and publish it. And we were able to create that world.

Our destiny gave us children this way; neither of us knew it.

If Bobby had listened to my begging before the time was right, or if I had thought long ago that Bobby would block me if I sent a photo like the one I sent him, these babies wouldn't have been able to hold on to my womb and wouldn't have been born. But we both went through a process that drove us crazy, and because we broke up at the right time, I was able to deliver these babies. No one and no event could destroy me anymore. I have had four babies from the greatest and eternal love of my life. From now on, I would exist only to keep them and my future babies alive. Everything else would be just minor details for me.

I examined my baby. Everything was perfect as far as

I could see. I ordered 20 books to quickly continue my plan in my new home and send them to specific libraries as a legal obligation. The next day, as soon as the books arrived, I signed and gave my books to the people at home, Lia and Jake. Lia had been working very hard and was very tired that day, "I will read it as soon as I get a chance," she said like everyone else.

When I woke up at nine o'clock the following day, I saw Lia's text. The first reader of my book, Lia, had messaged me at six in the morning and saying, "I opened the book to take a quick look before I went to sleep and couldn't put it down until I finished." After reading that long message that started with the word "Fantastic", I cried for several minutes.

That day, I saw one of the nextdoor neighbours; she had suggested to my housemates they all watch 'Love Island' together. "I like Love Island," I told her, which was a huge lie. I went to their house like a faceless person because they had ignored me and excluded me from the first moment we met. Because of them, even Josh had changed his behaviour towards me. What I saw and felt in the living room on the first night had come through loud and clear. I went next door with my books. I wrote a wildly exaggerated text on the book's first page, "To the members of my new family," signed and handed it to them.

They looked at me, rather taken aback, at a woman who had moved next door only a few days ago and whom they had had decided to exclude without even bothering to know her, writing them such a dedication. As they looked at me with that supercilious expression in their eyes, I announced I would be having a party for my book at the weekend. They asked me, "Will the party be crowded?"

"Only my housemates and your house members. I have no one but you in England. I am all alone here,"

I replied, just to compound their attitude towards me. They all looked at me, pity in their eyes, and said yes that they would definitely come to the party.

The next day I met my ex English teacher Anne-Marie and also Adam – whom I had met in York – and gave them each a copy of my book. Yes, I had never lost my friendship with Anne-Marie. She was my teacher for only fifteen days, but she had become like my older sister in England. Although we couldn't meet for a long time, we began to see each other regularly after writing my first book and Covid restrictions were over. What luck to find a sister in England like Anne-Marie. She might be the best, funniest, most friendly teacher, and sister in the world.

They read my book in three days and wrote me very long, complimentary messages too. With those proud messages from the first three readers of my book, Lia, Anne-Marie and Adam, I was smiling with self-confidence about my book and my feelings.

A few days later, it was the party. That my feelings could be so strong even frightened me as the time for the party to start came, and went.

Because no one came.

They had all gone to Victoria Park, five minutes from the house, to enjoy the beautiful weather, and did not return home until midnight. Except for Josh. He came home at nine o'clock and knocked on my door, but I didn't open it. It was too late. He had fallen in with them again.

"Are you home?" he texted.

"I'm in my room," I replied. But when he knocked on my door again, I didn't respond.

When the others returned home hours later, I continued to sit in my room alone in the dark. During those ten days in quarantine, I had prepared myself for this, knowing that a long battle of loneliness awaited me. However, when I faced it, I felt I had collapsed in those hours. I was ostracized by a group of people in a house I had just moved into, without their even wanting or bothering to get to know me. Even Josh, who I liked from the first moment I saw him, had started to behave like the others and exclude me. Jeff had not opened the door of my old home to me. Even though all the members of 3 Hilsea Street members found out about it, no one called me.

Although I felt ready, as I faced true loneliness, I began to walk like a grey shadow through Victoria Park. That vast, green space. When I reached the end of the park, a cliff thousands of feet high appeared in front of me. In my grey solitude, I looked back at that green park, the people in their colourful clothes, colouring that hot summer day; the groups of friends laughing; the families having fun; the joyful screams of children. And I dropped into that bottomless abyss. I was falling from a height of metres to crash into the ground at full speed, and I was experiencing hundreds of thousands of emotions simultaneously. My mind hunted those hundreds of thousands of emotions, transformed them into words and wrote that book of hundreds of lines.

Then, someone knocked on my door as I whimpered, "I wish you were with me, Otto," with tears in my eyes. Even though I didn't say "Come in", he opened the door softly, entered with a smile and sat next to me.

"You've got what you want. Now it's time to stay where you are," Daniel said, and I was lifted up into the air.

A giant iridescent coloured bird came, took me between its wings, and I began to soar through the sky between its soft wings.

"When I first started getting to know myself, I didn't know why you gave me the ability to show myself as a weak person in any new environment; I was angry with you," he said. "But over the years, I was amazed, I realized why you gave me this feature. You are crazy, brave and strong enough to introduce yourself as a weak and lonely person."

"Dreadful idea to always appear weak and to be alone if you can't escape out of it!"

"Come on, what have you been through and overcome? Now that you've fallen off that cliff, it's time to party," he said with a laugh. At that moment, the door opened wide, and first Louise, Angela, Carla, Keilee, Marcella, Alessia, Dustin, then Wilbert, Hena, Nisan and Sinem filed into the room. The voices of men and women who couldn't fit into the room came from outside saying, "Hi, we're here too".

While I was trying to see who they were, a pair of five-year-old twins, a girl and a boy, entered the room, jumped on my lap and hugged my neck, saying, "Mom".

I was staring at them and Daniel in amazement.

"You look like characters from an animation. What are you doing here?", I asked them, unable to understand.
"Because you will give birth to us like this," they said mischievously.
"When?"
"When Daniel has finished his battle and Wilbert his songs."
"Then I have to start working for you right away tomorrow, Daniel, huh?"
"No! First, finish what you have to do legally. Open a new Instagram account for your book, then write that book where you're going to finish your story, not mine. We can wait a little longer, can't we, girls?" he said, getting approval from his seven warriors.

"What am I going to write about? How my friends left me, how I was left alone, how Bobby never forgave me? It would be a great book of failure and loneliness! I can't. I can't write the end of the story!"

"You can write it. You even dared to write about what X did to you, and you lived in a garage in England for a year and a half. You have healed yourself while you were writing that book. You must bring the story to its end. You have to do this to become exactly the Dilek you want to be.

"Are you afraid? Do you feel alone?
"Look at the people in that room.
"Are you sure your friends left you?
"Wait a little.
"And Bobby?
"It's only been two days since you sent him the book. If you know him even a little bit, you know that he will go crazy for a few days, throw the book in anger. Then he will relax, but as he doesn't like reading, it will him take a long time to finish your thick book. Especially after the long messages that you sent him for months. Just wait. Everything starts again when it's over. Go to sleep. You know that in a few days, that time when you will be sleepless for days will begin again," he said.

I smiled.

"You also know how to write. Now you're between the wings of that bird; you've made it. You have seen that you are not afraid of being alone and you will never be a lonely person."

"Yes," I said, and Daniel and we hugged each other tightly.

Everyone began to leave my room, wishing me good night and telling me to hurry up, write my books quickly so that it would be their turn, in the hopes of getting together again as soon as possible. Everyone had gone out, except for one person. I didn't know this lovely English woman in an old Victorian dress, and I instantly felt she wasn't one of my children. She slowly approached me, sat next to me, took my hands in hers.

"Welcome to the real Bow Quarter," she said.
"Who are you?" I asked, a little startled.
"I'm Annie. I knew you would hear and come when I whispered to you, and I am so happy that you passed your trial today."

Goosebumps formed, my eyes filled with tears, "What do you mean, when I whispered to you?"

"I summoned you to the Bow Quarter, and you came, proved your courage, once again."

"Why did you call me here?"

"You will find out when the time comes. You have to finish the rest of the book first."

Looking at me with a loving yet determined gaze, she said, "I'm proud of you," and disappeared.

I took my phone, typed Bow Quarter and Annie into

Google. When I saw the picture of Annie Besant, the pioneer of the women's strikes in the factory, I froze. It was none other than the woman who had just stroked my cheek. Before I came to see this house, I didn't know anything about the Bow Quarter. I didn't even know there was such a place in London. But as I walked through the main door and Lia showed me around, a thousand calls had already filled my ears. However, even as a history lover, I was strangely unable to open and read the history of this place to satisfy my curiosity.

The day I moved this house, the first night I spent in my room, I couldn't sleep as always. I had gone for a walk in the garden of Bow Quarter, and stopped in front of the building to read the information panel on its history, but I gave up reading it inexplicably. Since then, every time I stood in front of it to read it, I had strangely given up and kept walking. That's why I didn't know about Annie's existence until she told me her name.

Then I started to think only about Annie and why I had come here, instead of being happy that I had overcome my fear of loneliness in a shorter time than I had anticipated.

When I opened my eyes in the morning, I was now that Dilek I wanted utterly. Even if they excluded me, turned away, made some ugly gesture and didn't turn back, I could forget about everyone and clean my heart and choose to continue on my way. And with this decision, I started finishing the legal work I had to do with my first book at full speed.

Two days after I started working with those thoughts, Giulia called me. She explained that she was very upset about what happened and wanted to meet me. We met in front of Liverpool Street Station on July 23. For about five minutes, we hugged each other, crying. Then we started laughing and hugging and crying again. Then we walked, excitedly investigating about five or six pubs, as we do every time we go out. Eventually, just when we were about to place our orders, we changed our minds again and left. Finally, we decided to go down the street opposite Liverpool Street Station and sat in the small but charming garden of the Fish Market, located at the end of the street. As usual, we looked at the cheapest items on the list and ordered the most expensive and good rosé wine and aperitifs. While we were waiting for a small plate, a huge seafood tray was served to us on ice. We poured our misunderstandings and resentments into the big thing in front of us and cleared up our problems one by one.

"Sorry, I wasn't home that time. If I were home, I would never let Jeff do that. I wanted to call you right after I learned what Jeff and Agata did, but I was too embarrassed. Then I got angry at you for calling Jeff before you came home, not me. Why didn't you call me?"

"Because you didn't call me. I told you that I was going to be treated for cancer. None of you was curious enough to call me."

"Dilek! We all knew that you told that lie because of Agata."

"Why didn't you say you understood?"

"Because we had argued. We had stopped speaking. You moved out of the house. You left me."

"I did not abandon you! On the contrary I turned our friendship into a reality."

"How so?"

"What are we doing now?"

"We are sitting down."

"And we are pointing out our mistakes and learning from them. We both hurt each other unintentionally, but we still didn't give up. We met again! We proved that we are not just two people who get along well because they live in the same house. Even though we've had our problems, we proved that we have a friendship that will last forever."

Giulia paused briefly, gave me her mischievous look, stood up and hugged me tightly. We drunk two bottles of wine, sitting there until the bar was closing. As always, we made fun of everything until we got to the bottom of the bullshit at some point or other. We laughed non-stop until we were irritating everyone around us with our laughter. Saying to me, "I am proud of you. You struggled for months and finally, you published that book. You did it!" she hugged and kissed me every ten minutes.

She couldn't resist any longer. "Why did you lie to us about the book until you started the translation? Why didn't you say the book was about us until that day came?" she asked.

"Because I didn't want any of you to change."

"You…," we laughed.

The restaurant was about to close. We were presented with a bill of around £150, and Giulia said, "Bullshit! They put a big tray in front of us, so big we couldn't seeing each other over it, but we could only eat five shrimps from it. The wine was good, but to pay that money for so much stale stuff... Porca Vacca," she said.

"You're right; we shouldn't be paying."
"Yes, we shouldn't pay."
"Then let's not pay."
"Let's not pay."
"There are no waiters in the garden at the moment. Let's wait two minutes and if no one comes, let's go quietly."
"Let's go! You are not serious, right now? No, you are serious!"
"Well, when I say let's do something, you know I will."
"So, how are we going to run away?"
"We will not run away; two minutes are up. We'll get our bags; we'll get up," I said. We stood up and walked arm in arm slowly towards the exit of the garden. We got out the door as we whispered, "If someone approaches, we will say, 'we were going to the checkout, but we were confused because we are drunk'." When we calmly left the restaurant behind, we suddenly started running at full speed to the back of Liverpool Street Station, laughing.

We asked each other, "What did we just do?" as we couldn't help laughing, regretting what we'd done. We started to scare each other. "What if there is a camera and the police catch us, cancel our visas and deport us?"

"Fortunately, you've already finished writing the book, so it won't go into the pages what we've done," said Giulia.

"Well," I said, laughing.

"What?"

"Of course, you don't know because you haven't read the book yet, but I created it as two books."

"How so? Will there be a sequel?"

"Yeah."

"All our arguments, our fights... At least don't write about what we did today, please. We committed a crime."

"Don't worry, when I sell the books and get rich, we'll come here together again and pay double the bill and pay off our debt."

"How far will you go in the second book? How many years?" she laughed.

"I will start writing it in a few days. So in a few days, this story will be completely over. No one knows that the book is currently on sale. Thus they won't get a chance to read the book. Promise me you won't tell the others that I'm going to write the sequel to the book," I said and made her swear many times. That evening, we returned to our homes with an even stronger bond than before.

The next day, I visited Stephen and Manuel. They had called me after Giula calls, and had invited me to their new home a day or so ago. "Our house is your house too. When you are bored, when you feel bad, come without thinking. Our door is always open to you," and they hugged me. A few days later, Stephen came to my house. He came to check how I was. We sat on the Bow Quarter terrace, drank our coffees there, and talked for hours.

So, I proved once again that I was doing the right thing. Jeff and Agata would no longer be in my life, but I had found a sister in Giulia and three real friends in Stephen, Manuel and Matt from my old home in 3 Hilsea Street. Now, I would continue on my way with my real friends who would stay firmly in my life in England. Moreover, not because we were housemates, sharing the same house, but as real friends.

It was time for the Bow Quarter to do the same. I had the opportunity to move into the empty room in Lia's house. Because I wasn't sure what she would do to me in the future, I didn't move to her house. And with all my good feelings I chose to stay with my housemates. Even though we started badly, I knew that I would get along well with my housemates as the day went on. And after meeting our new house member, Melanie, I was sure of that. Melanie was only twenty-two years old; we were sixteen years apart, I couldn't understand her accent exactly yet. However, she is a cool, intelligent and powerful girl; thus, I know we will be good friends.

And... absolutely my next-door neighbours were not that bad. On the contrary, they were very good people; they only had faulty behave traits. Like me, like everyone else, like all of us. So we should all deserve to give each other another chance.

On August 12, hours before I began to write the

sequel, I said, "I have a problem with the book cover," and collected my books from the people next door and the housemates. That was my first step.

Then whenever we came across each other at our bedroom doors, I would look at Josh as if to say, "Shame on you!" After a few days, Josh sent me a very long text. He apologized profusely, explaining how he was upset because of what he had done. "Also, you have a very different sensitivity, which is what I am not used to. Give me time to get used to that. Let's not stay angry with each other. I don't want to continue like this."

I nearly cried. It would be to my shame if I closed my arms and heart to Josh after that long and beautiful message. I forgave him and sent a long message explaining how I loved him as a friend. The Josh was back who I met on the first day that I moved in, who became my arms when I was in Turkey, who helped me in every way, who greeted me at the door with his tight embrace the day I returned.

Then I knocked on his door and asked, "Can I hug you?"
I will never forget that emotional smile and those wide-open arms.
"You'll have to get used to it," I said as I hugged him tightly.
"With great pleasure. Of course, instead of looking at me with anger, I would like you to hug me."

Yes, Josh, and I hugged each other. After what had happened, Josh and I both chose to solve our problems by talking, getting to know each other better, giving each other a chance and a hug.

We did.

But the others needed to learn too. They needed to understand how wrong it was to exclude a new person who had just entered their life without knowing them by succumbing to their biased feelings. The best way to do this was to hold a mirror up to them and show them themselves.

So I began to do to them the same things they did to me, but more so.

When I started to write my book, I went to the kitchen ten times a day and made my Turkish coffee. While in the kitchen, I wore my earphones, listening to music, and I never took them out. I ignored them. As I glanced into their eyes I turned away condescendingly. I made it very clear that I didn't give a toss about them.

As I did to them tenfold what they did to me, their attitude began to change. At first, they were surprised; they did not know what to do. Then they couldn't accept the stance I was taking towards them, and they ignored me again.

A few days later, Josh, the only person in common between them -the next door neighbours- and me, said, "I know it started badly, but how long are you going to continue like this? They are also upset about what happened."

"They don't look upset at all! I can go on until I see they are really sorry, that they understand what it means to be excluded, without a chance to express themselves. And if they don't understand, I can go on indefinitely using different methods."

After that conversation with Josh, they started to smile when they saw me. I didn't take the earphones out for the first few days and didn't respond to them, but I smiled back. When the others realized their mistake and took that tiny miraculous step and started smiling at me, I knew they were angry because they didn't understand why I still didn't encourage any conversation between us. As time progressed and near the end of the book, when I saw them, I didn't just smile, I took the earphones out of my ear and uttered those two magical questions, "How are you? Are you okay?"

We were all beginning to take a new step. Maybe we would get to know each other, love each other, and become firm friends. Maybe we would realize that we had no common ties, likes, shares, or pleasures, and we would walk away. But most important to finding that out was to give it a chance and try to understand each other. Did they have anything to lose by not doing that? Did I have anything to lose? Did any of us have anything to lose?

No.

But any understanding might be lost; the world might become an uglier place.

It isn't easy to try to understand each other, to try to live together. Maybe we will find it too hard, and we will be exhausted by it all. In the process, many of us might think that such effort is unnecessary and give up. Maybe some of us will turn to our own communities. In London, where I first set foot at the age of thirty-five, I could have chosen to live in my own community. Instead of criticizing them for cocooning themselves in those transparent bubbles – just like the communities of so many other societies – I could have stayed in that bubble I very nearly became stuck in. I could have given up looking for a room when I was rejected from dozens of houses because of my bad English. I have could given in, even returned to Turkey. Stephen might have chosen not to open the door to me at No. 3 Hilsea Street, not to have greeted me with his big smile or to have hugged me whenever I needed him. Matt might not have continued to encourage me as I tried to find my words. Even if I didn't understand what he was saying for the first month after I met him, Jeff could have got bored and might not have kept talking to me until the day came and I did understand him. Every time Giulia and I fell out, we might not have believed in the strength of our bond and chosen not to hug each other again in reconciliation.

I could have got tired and given up on everything before I even met them. After meeting me, they could have got tired and given up on me. Would there have been anything to lose in giving up?

No.

But there might be less belonging; immigrant mentality and racism would increase.

Josh, Melanie and I got along well, liked and hugged each other. But I know there would be so many tests for our friendship. Maybe we would pass these tests, turn those beautiful energies into tight, true friendships, just like at No. 3 Hilsea Street, and continue on our way. What would happen if we couldn't keep going? Would I lose anything? Would he lose anything? Would you lose anything?

No.

But friendships would die; humanity might perish.

No one has to love another person to be happy or proud of the other person's success. But we should not succumb to jealousy and have feelings of hate towards other people or exclude them. We all have inside of us, a devil. Some people manage to silence that devil, but some choose to worship it. Will Lia choose or manage to silence that devil that she has inside? Will I manage to silence that devil inside Lia? Will I manage to change the others' destructive emotions? Will I be able to rein in all their jealousy? Would it hurt me if I couldn't do this? Would it hurt them? Would it hurt you/us/other people?

No.

But goodness might die; the world would be corrupted.

Me, you, them, us… What would happen if we didn't learn to manage our jealousies, grudges, anger, hatred, discrimination, lies, hypocrisy, ostracism, humiliation and fears that penetrated our souls before we were born? Would we lose anything?

No.

Because we wouldn't exist anyway.
These books wouldn't exist either.

What would happen if I didn't throw all my life's difficulties aside and fight the real battle with myself, with those bad feelings that I have inside and want to destroy? It wasn't a lie. When the book came to the world after those words began to exist on the lines, I was a brand new Dilek. Because I learned to forgive people first. I even forgave the people I had decided not to meet again because of the wrongs they had done to me. When I thought about them, I learned to say, "They're not bad people; they're actually very nice people. They just acted in an unfortunate way towards me."

I even forgave X. In the six years I spent with him, I failed to change him, but maybe he had cured himself, or someone had come into his life and helped him.

I am a new Dilek, and that's how I treat those who come into my life. When someone takes one step towards me, I take ten steps, open my arms, and show the things that make me exist. If anyone understands them and dares to stand by me, I dare to understand them and stand by them, and we can hug each other tightly. We can go through many trials, but we know that we have to pass these tests and find strength on the way to that beautiful world. We can try to love and respect each other instead of being jealous, excluding, being angry with each other. When we break our hearts unintentionally, we can try to listen, understand each other. We can hug each other and heal each other's wounds. We can fall in love, and maybe we can fight to make that love exist and keep it alive.

You will too! You should! If you've read these two books, you should do it, even just one thing. At least you can try. Will I fail if you don't try? Will you fail? Will we fail?

No.

But those evil Gods in Daniel's world might win.

I will continue on my way with my arms open to all the people I come across in my life. I will always look at that glass shelf where I have carefully arranged and locked up all my bad feelings, memories and shortcomings, one by one. When I run out of energy, I will look at those evils that came out of me, and what I recreated, all the beauties in myself. If my fears, my bad feelings, my unfounded resentments grow, I will destroy them again by coming to the border of insanity every time if necessary. If I don't realize that they are growing or that they might already exist again, I will not be afraid or run away from that person when someone shows them to me, sees me better than I do, and understands them.

Don't run away either.

It is easier to run away from the one who shows you to yourself. Don't cover your ears and disappear when they try to reach out to you with all their might to heal you.

But take a step back.

Like Bobby.

Then take the hand of the person holding the mirror that shows the you inside you, and bring them in front of the mirror with you. Then both of you can see inside yourselves together and get rid of those evils that can feed on each other.

Do it too.

Just like Bobby did to me and like I did to Bobby. When you see each other's hearts, your flaws, fears, those evils that are hidden in those most secret places or that are all too obvious, you two will run away from each other. If one of you dares to take a step and the other chooses to only stop still instead of running away, you will have started that battle that will return you to the real you, which will either destroy you forever or bring you into existence. It will take a long time; it will be painful, sorrowful, heavy. You will not be able to stand it for a long time; you will fall, get tired, give up, get bored. You will question whether it is necessary. You will win despite all of this – if you keep on going, even if you crawl.

Both of you will win.

Maybe at the same time you'll end this battle. Maybe one of you, like Bobby and me, have reached that shore long ago. If you get tired of waiting for the one who struggles to continue that fight when you set foot on land, you will lose again if you leave that shore. If you keep waiting, like me, you must know that you have no choice but to wait, and wait, although you might get tired and question the reason for all that fighting in the first place...

You will win.
Like me.

As I continue to wait for Bobby to reach the shore, I won the very day I started writing this book. Three days after I started writing, I took a short break and opened a new Instagram account under my own name, to advertise my first book. While I completed transferring my profile to the business account, I came to the point where I needed to post to people I knew. I didn't want to spend too much time on all this, so I only sent the necessary post to the bogus account I had opened to follow Bobby months ago. I completed my transactions, shared a picture of my first baby and continued writing the sequel.

The following day, I saw a message notification on my Instagram. I had three Instagram accounts and checked them all to find out which one the message came from. I logged into my bogus account. "No, this cannot be!" I exclaimed. From that account, the link of my new account had gone to Bobby, and there was a message like "Hey, look, this is my new account, follow me" under it. That's when I realized that Bobby had blocked me there too. I returned to my new Instagram account that I had opened under my own name. I looked at Bobby's account. He hadn't blocked me from there. I texted him, "Bobby". He saw my message in an instant, those bubbles started flashing. For several minutes.

But he didn't send me a message.

I kept quiet and continued writing the book. Now I could see Bobby from my real Instagram account, but I stopped logging into his account again and checking what he posted after sending that message. I only opened my message box during the brief breaks I took and watched those bubbles flash.

His silence didn't drive me crazy anymore. I wasn't waiting for anything from him anymore. I was no longer the old Dilek. Maybe there wasn't even the tiniest emptiness in my heart anymore because of those stories that existed in it. I understood what his silence gave to me, and I gave birth to these four books. Now was his time to listen and understand my silence.

While I was waiting, I kept on writing. I did not know exactly what this wait would bring, but the only thing I was sure of was that I would not end the last lines of this book by calling out to Bobby.

And it happened just as I felt it would.

I had been writing on and on for eleven days, sleeping only one hour per day and without barely blinking for the last fifty-two hours. Today, Monday, August 23, 2021, at 1:36 p.m. I was writing that "But the only thing I was sure of was that I wasn't going to end the last lines of this book by calling out to him." As I finished it and typed the full stop at the end of the sentence, Bobby texted me, "Dilek".

At first, I thought it was a hallucination to see him texting me just as I was typing that sentence. But when I took the phone and checked it, I realized that it was real.

I replied, "Bobby", and those bubbles flashed again for minutes and then stopped.

I didn't write any more. I left him in his silence again. It was the truth. I did not expect anything from him anymore.

I took a deep breath and looked at the computer screen again to write my last lines, but I was distracted and forgot what to write. While trying to remember what to write, how to write, my eyes caught the sunlight hitting the wall of my room from my window. It was a beautiful day: the weather was warm, the sun was shining, and children were giggling. Young people were walking in the street laughing. Everyone had returned to their free life after that terrible year. But I was still captive in my room.

At the age of thirty-eight, I was trying to live in a room a monthly budget of seven hundred and fifty pounds. As if all the existing problems weren't enough, I had had to assemble an army with my loneliness, with my words, start Daniel's war with my next-door neighbours. Maybe I was tired, too tired. Still I was thrilled. Even if I died with Daniel and the battle waged by his seven warriors, I would die proud and happy. I could write a book a thousand pages long to describe that happiness. While I was looking at the sunlight on my wall, in that thought Daniel came and sat right next to me.

"The desolation is so loud," I told him.

He shook his head, "no".

He stretched out his right hand, closed the window and pulled the curtain to my left. At that moment, I saw a blue paint stain on his index finger. I was suddenly breathless. I frowned as I looked at him inexplicably.

Daniel was smiling slyly as he looked at me. "You're finally ready now," he said, holding out his blue paint-stained finger over the wide emptiness that stood in my heart's place.

I got it.

"It was always you!"

I said to him, my voice hoarse with amazement.

"It will always be you!"

he said, dipping his painted finger into the huge void.

A blue light appeared in the middle of my chest, filling the room, and we were thrown into the blue sky. To the sky of Daniel's world.

And I saw.

I saw every detail of what had happened in Daniel's world for twenty years from that sky. As I fell back into the room, horrified at what I had seen, Daniel placed my fingers on my keypad, put my headphones over my ears, and turned on a song.

"Here we are, don't turn away now / We are the warriors that built this town / From dust / Will come / When you'll have to rise / Above the best and prove yourself / Your spirit never dies!"

I smiled while listening to the song. I looked at the screen and tried to remember what I wanted to write again. "I wish Bobby and I were two characters in these books, and the story could finish with a happy ending. But we are real people in the real world. And the sparkling colours of love cannot exist or show themselves under the bright sunlight of the real world. That's why love dies in the real world."

Was I going to write this? It was so clichéd! This was not what I wanted to write, but I couldn't remember what to write.

I wonder why?

Maybe I stopped believing in that dream I had six months ago and the warmth that still grips my heart, after what I saw in Daniel's world.

Maybe my love was already dead too, long time ago.

Maybe I will continue to love Bobby too much, forever.

Maybe Bobby will stretch his hand out to me by saying, "I love you so much. Let's try again."

Maybe he will close his door completely, telling me, "Don't contact me again."

Maybe he will get scared again and run away forever, saying to me, "I love you so much, but we can't do it. Accept it."

Maybe he will tell me, "I have had someone else in my life for a long time", share his picture with her on Instagram.

Maybe we will get back together and prove that there is such a thing as love. Or we will have failed and killed a miraculous love with our very own hands.

But no matter what he tells me, I will be happy for him because he is a person who can find himself in his colours and paintings and can exist with them. I know his fragile, pure and clean heart, and I will remember him like that in my dreams in my heart forever. Although he loved me, he is a person who is afraid of not being able to touch those colours and not painting again. And I have no power but to understand this fear, to respect it, to accept it.

Whatever he will say to me, I will be happy for him. Because Bobby was the only reason why I stayed in England, no matter what I went through. That strange feeling that encompassed my heart brought me back every time. I only tried to find out what those feelings were and seek out the owner of the blue stained finger. It was Bobby who trapped me in his silence after it had come true, who couldn't manage to leave me until the time had to come, who could endure those messages that no human being could endure. It was Bobby who, for the first and last time in my life, looked at me with such pure, innocent eyes full of love and pain, said "I love you," and inhaled me in until his last breath with his petrified body. It was Bobby who lent me his colours when I couldn't write on the blank lines of the page before me, introducing me to pictures and colours and keeping me sane until it was time to write. Bobby is the father of my four babies that fell into my womb that first night we saw each other.

But I was the one who managed to get these things right, from him, like what I took from the others. I was the one who could see everything with its good side, wanted to see it and moved on. It was me who transformed me into the new me, who chose to change me, and who suffered the same pain that no one else has suffered on this path.

It was always me!
And
It will always be me!

You can be too. You can do the same. You can choose the right things from the people who come into your life, even from the worst person, and make them turn you into a better person and offer you new abilities. Maybe you write books like me, draw pictures like Bobby, or compose songs like Wilbert. Maybe when you need a friend or relative, you hug them tightly, you object to injustice, you say "good morning" to someone, you make them start the day well. You can smile at a person you don't know who is upset and having a bad day; you could make them happy again. You can say "thank you" to someone, be polite. Maybe you can grow a flower in a pot, stroke the head of a cat on the street. You don't have to be a superhero who takes up weapons and sets out to save the world. The day you discover that the most incredible and challenging skill is to have love, understanding, and to share it with people you never knew, you can become one of the superheroes who save the world.

Of course, if you dare.

I will try to dare it. I am waiting with my arms wide open but with my huge long-handled umbrella by my side. I wait with my umbrella knowing that good intentions are the most attractive and delicious prey for hunters. When I realize that those approaching me are one of these hunters, I will drive them away with the tip of that giant umbrella. If they come at me with armies, I will open my umbrella and fight them with my own huge army pouring out and surrounding me with my family, friends, Daniel, his warriors, Wilbert and more.

Open your arms wide, but also try to hold on to that umbrella in your life. If the day comes, and you open that umbrella, and you can't see a single person next to you, then go back and question yourself. Is it just because you're unlucky or because you hurt the people around you?

Dare to question yourself.

That's all I can tell you.

As my dear mother, Feride Ataönder, asked me at the age of five,

"So what is the main idea of this story?
When did this story actually begin?
How did this story grow up?
So, how did this story end?

I will not answer these questions for you. If you can't answer them, it means these two books are bullshit, plain and simple. If you understood even a single word that I have tried to tell you, you will answer these questions. And it means I have succeeded. I will be able to see that I have succeeded in this or not, by the fact that you are reading these lines, maybe in a few months, maybe in a few years. Maybe I will never be able to see this while I am alive.

I can't know that.

I don't know either what Bobby wrote to me just a few seconds ago. I will find out what he has told me when I turn off my computer and read the message he wrote to me, but you will not. At least from my lines. Because I will never write about my own life again.

My story has ended here.

Now is the time to bring to the world my other babies, who are waiting to be born and to grow up.

I will translate this book, which I wrote half in English and half in Turkish, into English at Caffé Nero next to the BBC. I have a plan so that you can read these books and be aware of what I write. If you read these two books, it means I succeeded in my plan.

As I write these last lines, the date is August 23, 2021, at 1:45 pm. I'll turn off my computer in a few seconds, read what Bobby has written to me, and sleep for a long, long time to heal my fifty-two hours of insomnia. After I wake up, I will eat a lovely meal, then swim in the Bow Quarter pool that I haven't had a chance to use yet and open my bones. I will go to Victoria Park and watch green London, the children screaming for joy, the happy people. I will listen to the rustle of the leaves of the trees swaying in the wind.

I will rest.

I need to rest, because a translation process is waiting for me that might make my nose bleed from the stress.

I need to rest. As I have discovered that I have two homelands, blue Istanbul and green London, now I must work hard to find my lost language. I need to find my writing ability in English as well as in Turkish.

I need to rest because I'll have to spend countless nights wandering through the quiet and dark garden of the Bow Quarter and try to understand why Annie has summoned me.

You rest just like me.

We need to rest because there is a great war waiting for us. A war that Daniel and his seven warriors on seven continents have been preparing for twenty years. We need to be ready! As you can see, I have too many dark colours inside my stories no matter how I tried to use some softer colours. But I can't change the colours inside Daniel's world. I have to write what I saw there precisely.

Nevertheless, I am curious. Will Daniel and his warriors heal themselves of the pain and evil they have experienced during those twenty years, or will they create a new, far worse world with all that pain? So, we need to rest because we have countless adventures waiting for us.

THE END

Printed in Great Britain
by Amazon